Business Calculations Euro Edition

Shelagh Hand and Bernard Mulchrone

Gill & Macmillan

Gill & Macmillan Ltd
Hume Avenue
Park West
Dublin 12
with associated companies throughout the world
© Shelagh Hand and Bernard Mulchrone 2001
www.gillmacmillan.ie

0 7171 3202 1

Typeset by
Mathematical Composition Setters Ltd, Salisbury, Wiltshire

The paper used in this book comes from the wood pulp of managed forests. For every tree felled, at least one tree is planted, thereby renewing natural resources.

A catalogue record is available for this book from the British Library.

Contents

CHAPTER 1

Basic arithmetical operations

In this chapter we will deal with:

Fractions
— **Adding, subtracting, multiplying and dividing fractions.**
— **Use of the word 'of'.**
— **Calculations involving combinations of arithmetic operations.**

Decimals
— **Converting decimals to fractions.**
— **Adding, subtracting, multiplying and dividing decimals.**

Percentages
— **Conversion of fractions and decimals to percentages.**
— **Conversion of percentages to fractions and decimals.**
— **Expressing one quantity as a percentage of another.**
— **Finding a number when given a percentage of that number.**
— **Percentage increase or decrease.**

There are exercises at the end of each section.

FRACTIONS

A fraction is a part of a whole number. For example, $\frac{5}{8}$ of an orange means that an orange has been divided into 8 parts and that we are interested in 5 of these parts. Fractions are part of everyday life, for example, we talk about $\frac{1}{2}$ of something, $\frac{1}{3}, \frac{1}{4}, \frac{1}{8}$ etc.

Fractions can be added, subtracted, multiplied and divided.

All fractions have two parts, separated by a line. The top part of the fraction is called the *numerator*. The lower part of the fraction is called the *denominator*. In the case of the fraction $\frac{5}{8}$, 5 is the numerator and 8 is the denominator.

A fraction where the numerator is smaller than the denominator is called a *proper fraction*. Examples are $\frac{4}{8}$ and $\frac{3}{8}$.

A fraction where the numerator is greater than the denominator is called an *improper fraction*. (It is sometimes also called a top heavy fraction). Examples are $\frac{9}{8}$ and $\frac{14}{8}$.

A number made up of whole numbers and fractions is called a *mixed number*. Examples are $1\frac{4}{5}$ and $3\frac{6}{7}$.

Note: A fraction should always be given in its lowest form. This means that before we add or subtract fractions, we should find the lowest common denominator or the lowest common multiple (LCM). This is the lowest whole number (integer) into which the denominator of the fractions will go evenly.

Example 1

Find the lowest common multiple of $\frac{1}{3} + \frac{2}{9} + \frac{3}{18}$.

Answer

Use the following procedure to get the LCM.

1. Look at the biggest denominator – in this case 18.

2. Will the other denominators divide into it exactly? In this case will 3 and 9 divide into 18 exactly? Yes, they will.

3. Therefore the LCM is 18.

Addition of fractions

Example 2

Add $\frac{1}{3} + \frac{2}{9} + \frac{3}{18}$.

Answer

First we must find the LCM, which is 18 (see previous section).

The next step is to divide each denominator into the LCM and multiply the corresponding numerator by the result. Therefore $\frac{1}{3}$ becomes $\frac{6}{18}$, $\frac{2}{9}$ becomes $\frac{4}{18}$ and $\frac{3}{18}$ remains $\frac{3}{18}$.

We can now add the fractions in the new form as follows:

$$\frac{6}{18} + \frac{4}{18} + \frac{3}{18}$$

$$= \frac{6 + 4 + 3}{18}$$

$$= \frac{13}{18} \text{ (this is a } \textit{proper fraction)}$$

Example 3

Add $\frac{2}{5} + \frac{6}{8} + \frac{1}{20}$.

Answer

Follow the procedure above to obtain the LCM. The biggest numerator is 20. The other numerators 5 and 8 will not divide into 20 exactly. The next step is to find a multiple of 20 that 5 and 8 will divide into exactly. We do this by going upwards through the 20 times table to find a number that 5 and 8 will divide into exactly.

$$20 \times 2 = 40$$

5 and 8 will divide into 40
Therefore our LCM is 40.
Now divide each denominator in turn into 40 and multiply the corresponding numerator by the result

$$= \frac{16 + 30 + 2}{40}$$

$= \frac{48}{40}$ (this is an *improper fraction*)
$= 1\frac{8}{40}$ (this is a *mixed number*)

Addition of mixed numbers

Example 4

Add $1\frac{2}{3} + 6\frac{1}{3} + 1\frac{2}{9}$.
Note: We are now dealing with whole numbers as well as fractions.

Answer

First add the whole numbers $= 1 + 6 + 1 = {}^{*}8$
Now add $\frac{2}{3} + \frac{1}{3} + \frac{2}{9}$ using the method in Example 2
LCM is 9

$$= \frac{6 + 3 + 2}{9}$$

$= \frac{11}{9}$

This gives $1\frac{2}{9}$
Total is ${}^{*}8 + 1\frac{2}{9} = 9\frac{2}{9}$
We could have solved this exercise in an alternative way. We could have turned each of the mixed numbers into an improper fraction and added these using the method in Example 2.

Alternative answer

$1\frac{2}{3} + 6\frac{1}{3} + 1\frac{2}{9}$
Convert the mixed numbers into improper fractions.
To do this first multiply the whole number (integer) by the denominator, add the result to the numerator and place the answer over the denominator.
Therefore $1\frac{2}{3}$ becomes $\frac{5}{3}$
$6\frac{1}{3}$ becomes $\frac{19}{3}$
$1\frac{2}{9}$ becomes $\frac{11}{9}$. Now the question is $\frac{5}{3} + \frac{19}{3} + \frac{11}{9}$

LCM is 9

$$= \frac{15 + 57 + 11}{9}$$

$$= \frac{83}{9}$$

9 will go into 83 9 times with $\frac{2}{9}$ over

$$= 9\frac{2}{9}.$$

Exercise 1.1

1. Add the following fractions:
   (a) $\frac{1}{2} + \frac{2}{3} =$
   (b) $\frac{2}{3} + \frac{1}{4} + \frac{1}{2} =$
   (c) $\frac{2}{3} + \frac{1}{5} =$
   (d) $\frac{3}{20} + \frac{4}{5} + \frac{5}{8} =$
   (e) $\frac{1}{2} + \frac{3}{4} + \frac{3}{5} + \frac{5}{8} =$
   (f) $\frac{6}{7} + \frac{2}{3} + \frac{9}{21} =$

2. Add the following mixed fractions:
   (a) $14\frac{1}{2} + 3\frac{4}{6} + \frac{5}{9} =$
   (b) $2\frac{5}{8} + 2\frac{6}{3} + 3\frac{9}{12} =$
   (c) $3\frac{2}{7} + 5\frac{1}{3} + 3\frac{15}{21} =$
   (d) $5\frac{4}{12} + 2\frac{4}{6} + 4\frac{1}{4} =$
   (e) $10\frac{1}{2} + 5\frac{6}{10} + 3\frac{1}{5} =$
   (f) $5\frac{1}{6} + 4\frac{9}{12} + 4\frac{19}{36} =$

Subtraction of fractions

Fractions are subtracted using the same procedure as for addition.
The first step is to find the LCM and then convert each of the fractions to this denominator.
Then subtract the numerators. If necessary, cancel the resulting fraction to its lowest form.

Example 5

Subtract $\frac{3}{4} - \frac{1}{8}$

Answer

LCM is 8.

$$\frac{6 - 1}{8} = \frac{5}{8}$$

Subtracting mixed numbers

Example 6
Subtract $8\frac{1}{2} - 1\frac{1}{5}$

Answer
$$8\frac{1}{2} - 1\frac{1}{5}$$
$$= 7\frac{1}{2} - \frac{1}{5}$$
$$= \frac{15}{2} - \frac{1}{5}$$
$$= \frac{75 - 2}{10}$$
$$= \frac{73}{10}$$
$$= 7\frac{3}{10}$$

Exercise 1.2
1. Subtract the following fractions:
   (a) $\frac{2}{3} - \frac{1}{9} =$
   (b) $\frac{5}{6} - \frac{3}{8} =$
   (c) $\frac{5}{8} - \frac{1}{3} =$
   (d) $\frac{13}{15} - \frac{3}{10} =$
   (e) $\frac{1}{4} - \frac{1}{8} =$
   (f) $\frac{4}{5} - \frac{8}{15} =$

2. Subtract the following fractions:
   (a) $1\frac{7}{10} - 1\frac{1}{2} =$
   (b) $2\frac{9}{11} - 1\frac{4}{11} =$
   (c) $14\frac{3}{10} - 8\frac{2}{5} =$
   (d) $8\frac{7}{8} - 5\frac{4}{5} =$
   (e) $6\frac{3}{4} - 3\frac{2}{5} =$
   (f) $15\frac{3}{7} - 7\frac{4}{5} =$

Multiplication of fractions

The LCM is not needed to multiply fractions. Simply multiply the numerators by each other and similarly the denominators by each other. Look at the following example.

Example 7

$$\text{Multiply } \overset{\frown}{\frac{4}{8}} \times \overset{\frown}{\frac{12}{16}} \times \overset{\frown}{\frac{3}{4}}$$

Answer

$$\frac{4 \times 12 \times 3}{8 \times 16 \times 4}$$

$$= \frac{144}{512}$$

We can simplify this fraction by dividing the numerator and denominator by 8, i.e. we have found a number which divides into both numerator and denominator evenly

$$= \frac{18}{64}$$

This can be further simplified by dividing the top and bottom by 2.
Therefore the answer $= \frac{9}{32}$.

This process is called *cancelling*. We could have started solving the above example in the first place by cancelling the figure 4 below the line with the figure 4 above the line. Please see the next example.

Example 8

Multiply $\frac{4}{8} \times \frac{12}{16} \times \frac{3}{4}$.

Answer

Cancel the 4 above the line with the 4 below the line twice

$$= \frac{\cancel{4}^1}{8} \times \frac{\cancel{12}^3}{\cancel{16}_4} \times \frac{3}{\cancel{4}_1} = \frac{9}{32}$$

Note: The value of a fraction is not changed if the numerator and denominator are each multiplied or divided by the same number.

Exercise 1.3

1. Multiply these fractions:
    (a) $\frac{1}{3} \times \frac{3}{4} =$
    (b) $\frac{3}{7} \times \frac{5}{8} =$
    (c) $\frac{1}{3} \times \frac{7}{10} =$
    (d) $\frac{3}{8} \times \frac{5}{9} =$
    (e) $\frac{17}{20} \times \frac{5}{16} =$
    (f) $\frac{14}{15} \times \frac{9}{12} =$

2. Multiply these fractions
   (a) $\frac{7}{11} \times \frac{9}{10} \times \frac{20}{22} =$
   (b) $\frac{6}{7} \times \frac{8}{9} \times \frac{16}{17} =$
   (c) $\frac{2}{7} \times \frac{3}{5} \times \frac{15}{16} =$
   (d) $\frac{3}{4} \times \frac{19}{21} \times \frac{6}{10} =$
   (e) $\frac{7}{10} \times \frac{4}{15} \times \frac{15}{16} =$
   (f) $\frac{11}{12} \times \frac{3}{4} \times \frac{4}{9} =$

Multiplication of mixed numbers

The best way to multiply mixed numbers is by first changing them into improper fractions. Then multiply the numerators and denominators in the usual way, cancelling down if possible. If the result is itself an improper fraction, then convert it into a mixed number.

Example 9

Multiply $2\frac{5}{8} \times 3\frac{2}{3}$.

Answer

First change into improper fractions

$$= \frac{21}{8} \times \frac{11}{3}$$

Now cancel above and below by 3

$$= \frac{\cancel{21}^{7}}{8} \times \frac{11}{\cancel{3}_{1}}$$

$$= \frac{7}{8} \times \frac{11}{1}$$

$$= \frac{77}{8}$$

Now convert this to a mixed number

$$= 9\frac{5}{8}$$

Exercise 1.4

1. Multiply these mixed numbers
   (a) $2\frac{1}{2} \times 3\frac{1}{3} =$
   (b) $10\frac{1}{4} \times 11\frac{1}{7} =$
   (c) $2\frac{3}{4} \times 3\frac{2}{11} =$
   (d) $2\frac{1}{3} \times 2\frac{3}{4} \times 2\frac{2}{9} =$
   (e) $5\frac{2}{3} \times 1\frac{1}{2} \times 1\frac{2}{31} =$
   (f) $3\frac{7}{8} \times 3\frac{1}{3} \times 1\frac{1}{5} =$
   (g) $1\frac{7}{8} \times 3\frac{3}{5} \times 2\frac{1}{7} =$

Division of fractions

The rule for dividing fractions is to *turn the divisor upside down and multiply*.

Example 10

Divide 20 by $\frac{1}{4}$.

Answer

$$20 \div \frac{1}{4}$$
$$= \frac{20}{1} \times \frac{4}{1}$$
$$= 80$$

Example 11

Divide $\frac{1}{3}$ by $\frac{5}{8}$.

Answer

$$\frac{1}{3} \div \frac{5}{8}$$
$$= \frac{1}{3} \times \frac{8}{5}$$
$$= \frac{8}{15}$$

Example 12

Divide $\frac{3}{4}$ by 2.

Answer

$$\frac{3}{4} \div 2$$
$$= \frac{3}{4} \div \frac{2}{1}$$
$$= \frac{3}{4} \times \frac{1}{2}$$
$$= \frac{3}{8}$$

Dividing mixed fractions

To divide mixed fractions simply change them into improper fractions, turn the divisor upside down and multiply as before.

Example 13

Divide $2\frac{3}{4}$ by $1\frac{1}{3}$.

Answer

$$2\tfrac{3}{4} \div 1\tfrac{1}{3}$$
$$= \tfrac{11}{4} \div \tfrac{4}{3}$$
$$= \tfrac{11}{4} \times \tfrac{3}{4}$$
$$= \tfrac{33}{16}$$
$$= 2\tfrac{1}{16}$$

Exercise 1.5

1. Divide the following fractions:
   (a) $\tfrac{3}{4} \div \tfrac{3}{8} =$
   (b) $\tfrac{2}{9} \div \tfrac{18}{19} =$
   (c) $\tfrac{4}{11} \div \tfrac{11}{16} =$
   (d) $\tfrac{3}{9} \div \tfrac{9}{27} =$
   (e) $\tfrac{11}{13} \div \tfrac{4}{7} =$
   (f) $\tfrac{22}{31} \div \tfrac{19}{20} =$

2. Divide the following mixed fractions:
   (a) $1\tfrac{2}{3} \div 2\tfrac{3}{8} =$
   (b) $16\tfrac{1}{7} \div 1\tfrac{2}{7} =$
   (c) $19\tfrac{1}{7} \div 21\tfrac{1}{6} =$
   (d) $2\tfrac{5}{8} \div 3\tfrac{6}{7} =$
   (e) $9\tfrac{7}{9} \div 6\tfrac{7}{21} =$
   (f) $23\tfrac{1}{3} \div 5\tfrac{1}{4} =$

Use of the word 'of'

Note: Sometimes the word 'of' can cause confusion in mathematics. In mathematics 'of' means 'multiplied by'. See the following examples.

Example 14

Find $\tfrac{1}{2}$ of 8.

Answer

$$\tfrac{1}{2} \times \tfrac{8}{1} = 4$$

Example 15

Find $\tfrac{1}{4}$ of 12.

Answer

$$\tfrac{1}{4} \times \tfrac{12}{1} = 3$$

Example 16

Find $\frac{5}{6}$ of $3\frac{3}{10}$.

Answer

$$\frac{5}{6} \times \frac{33}{10}$$

Cancel 3 into 33 and 6, cancel 5 into 5 and 10

$$= \frac{1}{2} \times \frac{11}{2}$$
$$= \frac{11}{4}$$
$$= 2\frac{3}{4}$$

Exercise 1.6

1. (a) Find $\frac{1}{3}$ of 9.
   (b) Find $\frac{1}{2}$ of 240.
   (c) Find $\frac{1}{4}$ of 200.
   (d) Find $\frac{1}{8}$ of 16.

Calculations involving combinations of arithmetic operations

Sometimes a question may include addition, subtraction, multiplication and division.
Note: It is very important to remember that multiplication and division must be done before addition and subtraction.

Example 17

Solve the following: $2\frac{2}{5}(4\frac{2}{3} + 2\frac{5}{6}) - 3\frac{3}{4} \div 2\frac{1}{2}$

Answer

$$2\frac{2}{5}(6\frac{2}{3} + \frac{5}{6}) - \frac{15}{4} \div \frac{5}{2}$$

$$= \frac{12}{5}\left(6\,\frac{4+5}{6}\right) - \frac{15^{\,3}}{4_{\,2}} \times \frac{2^{\,1}}{5_{\,1}}$$

$$= \frac{12}{5} \times 7\frac{1}{2} - \frac{3}{2}$$

$$= \frac{12^{\,6}}{5_{\,1}} \times \frac{15^{\,3}}{2_{\,1}} - \frac{3}{2}$$

$$= 18 - 1\frac{1}{2}$$
$$= 16\frac{1}{2}$$

Exercise 1.7

1. (a) $\frac{3}{4}\left(\frac{1}{3}+\frac{2}{5}\right)$

   (b) $1\frac{1}{3}\left(3\frac{1}{3}+6\frac{1}{9}\right)-1\frac{1}{3}$

   (c) $\left(6\frac{1}{4}+4\frac{3}{8}\right)\times\left(\frac{2}{9}-\frac{1}{18}\right)$

   (d) $\left(9\frac{2}{5}\div\frac{1}{10}\right)-1\frac{1}{5}\left(6\frac{2}{3}+4\frac{5}{6}\right)$

   (e) $21\frac{1}{4}-\frac{1}{8}\left(\frac{1}{16}+\frac{2}{24}\right)$

DECIMALS

We now know that a fraction is a part of a unit and that this is expressed by placing one number (the numerator) over another (the denominator), e.g. $\frac{1}{2}, \frac{2}{3}, \frac{3}{4}$.

There is another way in which a fraction may be expressed, i.e. by using the decimal system. The word decimal comes from the Latin word *decem* which means 10.

A decimal fraction is so-called because it is expressed as part of 10, or as a fraction of a multiple of 10. For example, $\frac{5}{100}, \frac{25}{100}$, etc.

The *decimal point* is a dot which separates the whole number from the part number. After the decimal point, the first place is for $\frac{1}{10}$ths, the second place is for $\frac{1}{100}$ths etc.

For example, if we take 2.186, the digit 1 has value $\frac{1}{10}$, the digit 8 has the value $\frac{8}{100}$ and the digit 6 has the value $\frac{6}{1000}$.

Converting decimals to fractions

Decimals may be converted into fractions as shown in the following example.

Example 18

Convert 1.186 to a fraction.

Answer

$$1.186 = 1 + \frac{1}{10} + \frac{8}{100} + \frac{6}{1000} = 1\frac{186}{1000}$$

Example 19

Convert 6.8 to a fraction.

Answer

$$6.8 = 6 + \frac{8}{10}$$

Now divide 8 and 10 by 2

$$= 6 + \frac{4}{5} = 6\frac{4}{5}$$

Example 20

Convert 12.11 to a fraction.

Answer

$$12.11 = 12 + \frac{1}{10} + \frac{1}{100} = 12 + \frac{11}{100} = 12\frac{11}{100}.$$

Converting fractions to decimals

Fractions can be converted to decimals by dividing the denominator into the numerator, as shown in the following examples.

Example 21

Convert $\frac{3}{5}$ to a decimal.

Answer

$$\text{Divide 5 into 3} \quad 5\overline{\smash{\big)}3.0} = 0.60.$$

Example 22

Convert $\frac{4}{100}$ to a decimal.

Answer

$$\text{Divide 100 into 4} \quad 100\overline{\smash{\big)}4.00} = 0.04.$$

Example 23

Convert $\frac{6}{1000}$ to a decimal.

Answer

Divide 1000 into $6 = 0.006$.

Note: Be very careful with the placing of the decimal point.

Exercise 1.8

1. What is the value of 6 in each of these? (Express each answer as a fraction.)
    (a) 1.675
    (b) 1.764
    (c) 8.756
    (d) 88.62

2. Write these as fractions in their lowest form:
    (a) 0.6
    (b) 0.7
    (c) 0.06
    (d) 0.007
    (e) 1.5
    (f) 0.16

3. Write these as decimals:
   (a) $\frac{6}{10}$
   (b) $\frac{7}{100}$
   (c) $\frac{4}{1000}$
   (d) $\frac{12}{100}$
   (e) $\frac{21}{1000}$
   (f) $4\frac{1}{10}$

Addition and subtraction of decimals

When adding and subtracting numbers which have decimal fractions, *always keep the decimal points underneath one another*.

This brings units under units, tens under tens, hundreds under hundreds on one side of the decimal point; on the other side, the tenths will be under the tenths, the hundredths under hundredths etc.

Example 24

Add the following numbers: 1.16, 1.176, 2.89 and 6.742.

Answer

Note: It is advisable to place the largest number on top.

```
   6.742
   2.89
   1.176
   1.116
  _____

  11.968
```

Example 25

Subtract 6.84 from 64.241.

Answer

```
   64.241
   -6.84
  _____

   57.401
```

Exercise 1.9

1. Add the following:
   (a) $62.48 + 16.50 + 16.99 + 27.94 =$
   (b) $45.42 + 64.99 + 31.71 + 68.49 =$
   (c) $124.68 + 1.72 + 19.624 + 9.024 =$
   (d) $897.02 + 999.99 + 178.95 + 263.974 =$
   (e) $1987.5 + 2977.48 + 2.972 + 6.5 =$
   (f) $589.62 + 997.456 + 2987.70 + 21.5 =$

2. Subtract the following:
    (a) 9.7 – 6.25 =
    (b) 68.72 – 45.5 =
    (c) 148.64 – 27.829 =
    (d) 998.25 – 2.786 =
    (e) 32 900 – 16.7821 =
    (f) 9764.21 – 84.666 =

Multiplication of decimals

The easiest way of multiplying decimals is to ignore the decimal points altogether until the end of the multiplication and only then to find the correct position of the decimal point in the answer.

Example 26

Multiply 2.68 by 2.1.

Answer

Step 1: Ignore the decimal points and carry out the multiplication in the normal way.

$$
\begin{array}{r}
2.68 \times \\
2.1 \\
\hline
268 \\
5360 \\
\hline
5.628
\end{array}
$$

Step 2: To find the position of the decimal point carry out the following procedure. Count the places after the decimal point in *both* sets of figures; there will be the same number of places after the decimal point in the answer.

In the above example there is one place after the decimal point in 2.1 and two places after the decimal point in 2.68. This means that there are three places after the decimal point altogether. Therefore there will be three places after the decimal point in the answer. The answer therefore is 5.628.

Exercise 1.10

1. Multiply the following:
    (a) 6.82 × 2.1 =
    (b) 8.97 × 6.5 =
    (c) 97.2 × 28.1 =
    (d) 269.786 × 0.928 =
    (e) 9.66 × 2.9 =
    (f) 672.5 × 99.04 =
    (g) 729.4 × 0.52 =
    (h) 628.997 × 0.624 =
    (i) 829.7 × 1.97 =

Multiplying and dividing decimals by multiples of 10

To multiply by 10, move the decimal point 1 place to the right;
to multiply by 100 move the decimal point 2 places to the right;
to multiply by 1000 move the decimal point 3 places to the right and so on for further multiples of 10.
The opposite applies when dividing by 10, 100 etc., i.e. the decimal point is moved to the left.

Example 27

Multiplication

$2.689 \times 10 = 26.89$
$2.689 \times 100 = 268.9$
$2.689 \times 1000 = 2\ 689.$

Division

$2.689 \div 10 = 0.2689$
$2.689 \div 100 = 0.02689$
$2.689 \div 1\ 000 = 0.002689$

Exercise 1.11

1. Multiply the following:
   (a) $62.7 \times 10 =$
   (b) $42.976 \times 10 =$
   (c) $629.1 \times 10 =$
   (d) $1285.268 \times 10 =$
   (e) $129.42 \times 100 =$
   (f) $26.748 \times 1000 =$

2. Divide the following:
   (a) $62.97 \div 10 =$
   (b) $697.24 \div 100 =$
   (c) $697.24 \div 1000 =$
   (d) $298.2 \div 10 =$
   (e) $67.24 \div 1000 =$
   (f) $1976.1 \div 100 =$

Division of decimals

The simplest way to divide by a decimal is to change the divisor so that it becomes a whole number, e.g. $5.2 \div 2.6$. The only way to remove the decimal point in this case is to multiply by 10. Thus $10 \times 2.6 = 26$. But in order to compensate for this change we must do the same to the dividend, i.e. $5.2 \times 10 = 52$. Therefore the calculation now becomes $52 \div 26 = 2$.
Note: To divide decimals, change the divisor to a whole number, and move the decimal point the same number of places in the dividend.

Example 28

Find $128.674 \div 6.7$.

Answer

First change the divisor to a whole number

> i.e. $6.7 \times 10 = 67$

Now we must also multiply the dividend by 10, i.e. $128.674 \times 10 = 1286.74$
Therefore the question is now $1286.74 \div 67$

> $= 19.20574$

Note 1: To 2 decimal places the answer is 19.21.
Note 2: Some divisions do not work out exactly, but the division process goes on and on.

Example 29

Find $100 \div 3$.

Answer

> $100 \div 3 = 33.333 \ldots$

The figure 3 recurs forever. This is known as a recurring decimal.

Example 30

Express $\frac{3}{7}$ as a decimal.

Answer

> $3 \div 7 = 0.4285$

In divisions like these, the answer is usually required to a certain degree of accuracy, for example, correct to 2 decimal places. If the calculation comes to 68.4967, accuracy to $\frac{1}{100}$ of a unit gives an answer of 68.50.

Rounding off and dividing decimals

Exercise 1.12

1. Round off each of the following to 2 decimal places:
   (a) 64.703
   (b) 157.3562
   (c) 105.986
   (d) 1.085

2. Divide the following correct to 2 decimal places:
    (a) $2.5 \div 1.6 =$
    (b) $98.62 \div 7.9 =$
    (c) $45.789 \div 2.7 =$
    (d) $667.2 \div 9.6 =$
    (e) $1\ 297.1 \div 2.5 =$
    (f) $976.256 \div 2.9 =$
    (g) $72.77 \div 5.9 =$
    (h) $66.741 \div 2.96 =$
    (i) $1267.42 \div 29.74$

PERCENTAGES

The word *percentage* comes from the Latin word for 100, *centum*. Per means 'out of'. Therefore percentage means 'out of 100'. The % sign is used for 'per cent', so that, for example, 20 per cent = 20%.

If you are told that in a school, 20% of the students come from a rural background, then this means that out of every 100 pupils in the school, 20 of them have a rural background.

Frequently used percentages

$$\frac{3}{4} = \frac{75}{100} = 75\%$$
$$\frac{1}{2} = \frac{50}{100} = 50\%$$
$$\frac{1}{4} = \frac{25}{100} = 25\%$$

$$\frac{1}{3} = \frac{33\frac{1}{3}}{100} = 33\frac{1}{3}\%$$

$$\frac{2}{3} = \frac{66\frac{2}{3}}{100} = 66\frac{2}{3}\%$$

$$\frac{1}{5} = \frac{20}{100} = 20\%$$
$$\frac{2}{5} = \frac{40}{100} = 40\%$$
$$\frac{1}{20} = \frac{5}{100} = 5\%$$

$$\frac{1}{8} = \frac{12\frac{1}{2}}{100} = 12\frac{1}{2}\%$$

$$\frac{1}{40} = \frac{1}{40} \times 100 = \frac{10}{4} = 2\frac{1}{2}\%$$

Note: Percentages are used:

(a) to make comparisons between numbers
(b) to express relationships between numbers.

Conversion of fractions and decimals to percentages

Fractions, decimals and percentages are frequently used in business. Therefore you should become familiar with their conversions.

Note: To change a fraction to a percentage, put down the fraction and multiply it by 100, as shown in the following examples.

Example 31

Change $\frac{1}{2}$ to a percentage.

Answer

$$\frac{1}{\cancel{2}_1} \times \frac{\cancel{100}^{50}}{1} = 50\%$$

Example 32

Change $\frac{1}{4}$ to a percentage.

Answer

$$\frac{1}{\cancel{4}_1} \times \frac{\cancel{100}^{25}}{1} = 25\%$$

Example 33

Change $\frac{3}{4}$ to a percentage.

Answer

$$\frac{3}{\cancel{4}_1} \times \frac{\cancel{100}^{25}}{1} = 75\%$$

Note: To change a decimal to a percentage multiply the decimal by 100 and put the % sign in the answer, as shown in the following examples.

Example 34

Change 0.50 to a percentage.

Answer

$$0.50 \times 100 = 50\%$$

Example 35

Change 0.25 to a percentage.

Answer

$$0.25 \times 100 = 25\%$$

Example 36

Change 0.2987 to a percentage.

Answer

$$0.2987 \times 100 = 29.87\%$$

Example 37

Change 1.25 to a percentage.

Answer

$$1.25 \times 100 = 125\%$$

Exercise 1.13

1. Convert the following fractions to percentages:
   (a) $\frac{5}{8}$
   (b) $\frac{3}{4}$
   (c) $\frac{2}{5}$
   (d) $\frac{9}{8}$
   (e) $\frac{2}{20}$
   (f) $\frac{1}{8}$
   (g) $\frac{1}{16}$
   (h) $1\frac{6}{16}$
   (i) $5\frac{7}{8}$
   (j) $8\frac{1}{2}$
   (k) $4\frac{2}{5}$

2. Convert the following decimals to percentages:
   (a) 0.52
   (b) 1.25
   (c) 0.6789
   (d) 6.27
   (e) 2.9678
   (f) 0.256
   (g) 0.976
   (h) 2.87

Conversion of percentages to fractions and decimals

Note: To convert a percentage to a fraction put down the whole number of the percentage as the numerator, and put down 100 as the denominator. Then cancel if possible, as shown in the examples below.

Example 38
Convert 74% to a fraction.

Answer

$$74\% = \frac{\cancel{74}^{37}}{\cancel{100}_{50}} = \frac{37}{50}$$

Example 39
Convert 25% to a fraction.

Answer

$$25\% = \frac{\cancel{25}^{1}}{\cancel{100}_{4}} = \frac{1}{4}$$

Example 40
Convert 75% to a fraction.

Answer

$$75\% = \frac{\cancel{75}^{3}}{\cancel{100}_{4}} = \frac{3}{4}$$

Example 41
Convert 120% to a fraction.

Answer

$$120\% = \frac{12\cancel{0}}{10\cancel{0}} = \frac{\cancel{12}^{6}}{\cancel{10}_{5}} = \frac{6}{5} = 1\frac{1}{5}$$

Example 42
Convert 20.5% = to a fraction.

Answer

$$20.5\% = \frac{20\frac{1}{2}}{100} = \frac{41}{200}$$

Note: To change a percentage to a decimal you put down the percentage and divide it by 100, as shown in the following examples.

Example 43

Convert 25% to a decimal.

Answer

$$25\% = 25.00 \div 100 = \tfrac{25}{100} = 0.25$$

Example 44

Convert 85% to a decimal.

Answer

$$85\% = 85.00 \div 100 = \tfrac{85}{100} = 0.85$$

Example 45

Convert 21.25% to a decimal.

Answer

$$21.25\% = 21.25 \div 100 = \tfrac{21.25}{100} = 0.2125$$

Example 46

Convert 125% to a decimal.

Answer

$$125\% = 125 \div 100 = \tfrac{125}{100} = 1.25$$

Exercise 1.14

1. Convert the following percentages to fractions in their lowest form.
   (a) 20%
   (b) 50%
   (c) 56%
   (d) 48%
   (e) $27\frac{1}{4}$%
   (f) 80%
   (g) $23\frac{1}{3}$%
   (h) $12\frac{5}{11}$%
   (i) 124%

2. Convert the following percentages to decimals.
   (a) 27%
   (b) 9.27%
   (c) 64%
   (d) 66.66%
   (e) 78%
   (f) 21%
   (g) 45%
   (h) 13%
   (i) 18.72%

Expressing one quantity as a percentage of another

Note: To express one quantity as a percentage of another, use the following:

$$\frac{\text{First quantity}}{\text{Second quantity}} \times \frac{100}{1} \%$$

Both quantities must be similar.

Example 47

What percentage is €10 of €20?

Answer

€10 is $\frac{10}{20}$ of €20

$\frac{10}{20}$ as a percentage is $\frac{10}{20} \times \frac{100}{1} = \frac{10}{1} \times \frac{5}{1} = 50\%$

Note: The smaller quantity is the numerator. The larger quantity is the denominator.

Exercise 1.15

1. Express the first quantity as a percentage of the second in each of the following.
   (a) 13, 50
   (b) 20 cents, €4
   (c) 28 cents, €1.40
   (d) 3, 4
   (e) €64, €100
   (f) 50 cents, €150
   (g) 10, 270
   (h) 70, 1 200
   (i) €45, €70

To find a percentage of a quantity

Note: To find a percentage of a quantity, write down the percentage required and multiply it by the original quantity.

Example 48
Find 6% of 2748.

Answer
6% of $2748 = \frac{6}{100} \times \frac{2748}{1} = 16\frac{488}{100} = 164.88$

Example 49
Find $12\frac{1}{2}\%$ of 567.

Answer

$12\frac{1}{2}\%$ expressed as a fraction is $\dfrac{12\frac{1}{2}}{100}$

Now change the whole number $= \dfrac{12\frac{1}{2} \times 2}{100 \times 2} = \dfrac{25}{200} = \frac{1}{8}$

$\frac{1}{8}$ of $567 = \frac{1}{8} \times \frac{567}{1} = 70.88$

Exercise 1.16
1. Find:
   (a) 20% of 968
   (b) 10% of 276
   (c) 50% of 1972
   (d) 90% of 29 763
   (e) 45% of €164
   (f) 25% of €742
   (g) 15% of €16 423
   (h) 21% of €70
   (i) 18% of 16
   (j) 75% of €92
   (k) 85% of 92
   (l) 92% of €60

2. Calculate the following percentage parts:
   (a) 52% of 480 kg
   (b) 25% of 50 km
   (c) 90% of 2000 litres
   (d) 50% of 870 litres
   (e) 40% of 800 km
   (f) 97% of 87 litres
   (g) 27% of 600 kg
   (h) 60% of 127 km

To find a number when given a percentage of that number

Example 50

20% of a number is 180. What is the number?

Answer

20% of a number is 180

$\quad$ 1% of that number is $\frac{180}{20}$

Therefore 100% (all of it) of that number is $\frac{180}{20} \times 100$

$\quad$ = 900

Percentage increase or decrease

Note: The amount of increase (or decrease) is always expressed as a percentage of the original amount.

Example 51

If the population of a town decreased from 20 000 to 15 000, what was the percentage decrease?

Answer

Actual decrease = 20 000 − 15 000 = 5000

$$\text{Percentage decrease} = \frac{5000}{20\ 000} \times 100$$

$$\text{We can now cancel above and below the line} = \frac{5\cancel{000}}{20\ \cancel{000}} \times 10\cancel{0}$$

$= \frac{5}{2} \times 10 = \frac{50}{2} = 25\%$

Percentage decrease = 25%

Example 52

A school has 630 students in 1997. This was an increase of $12\frac{1}{2}\%$ on the previous year. How many students attended the school in 1996?

Answer

Number of students in 1997 = 630
630 is made up of number of students in 1996 plus $12\frac{1}{2}\%$ increase

$\quad = 100\% + 12\frac{1}{2}\%$
$\quad = 112\frac{1}{2}\%$

so $112\frac{1}{2}\% = 630$ students

$$1\% = \frac{630}{112\frac{1}{2}}$$

$$100\% = \frac{630}{112\frac{1}{2}} \times 100$$

$$= 560$$

$$= 560 \text{ students.}$$

Exercise 1.17

Give your answers correct to two decimal places where necessary.

1. 18% of a number is 90. What is the number?

2. 25% of a number is 200. What is the number?

3. $2\frac{1}{2}\%$ of a number is 50. What is the number?

4. Increase 710 by 20%.

5. Increase 620 by 50%.

6. Decrease 280 by 15%.

7. A number is increased by 75%. If the new number is 8000, what was the original number?

8. A household commodity cost €400. The same product cost €430 a year later. What is the percentage increase?

Revision Exercise 1.18

Give your answers correct to two decimal places where necessary.

1. 50% of a number is 580. What is the number?
2. 14% of a sum of money is €60. What is the sum of money?
3. In a class of 40 students, 18 travel to school by bus. What percentage of the class is this?
4. Caroline obtained 80 marks out of a possible 150 in her business calculations examination. What was her percentage mark?
5. Mary earns €330 per week and saves €45 of this amount. What percentage of her money does she save? She spends 25% of her earnings on travel. Calculate the amount of money she spends on travel each week.
6. Patricia walks $\frac{1}{2}$ km to school and takes a bus for the remaining $2\frac{1}{2}$ km. What percentage of the total journey does she walk?

CHAPTER 2
The use of the electronic calculator

In this chapter we will deal with:
— a layout of a typical electronic calculator
— definition of the main key functions
— Euro currency conversion
— exercises on using the electronic calculator.

$\boxed{\text{MR}}$ This puts the number in the memory back on display.

To clear the memory, switch the calculator off and on again. Or press $\boxed{\text{MC}}$ / $\boxed{\text{CM}}$ or press $\boxed{\text{MRC}}$ / $\boxed{\text{RCM}}$ twice.

Example

$99 - (4 \times 6) + (15 - 3) =$

Press: 93 $\boxed{\text{M+}}$

$4 \times 6 = \boxed{\text{M-}}$

$15 - 3 = \boxed{\text{M+}}$

$\boxed{\text{MR}}$ 81

Now try the following:

1. $(6 \times 4) - (8 - 2) - (2 - 3) =$ (Answer: 12)
2. $(36 - 6) - (10 - 5) + (10 \times 6) =$ (Answer: 85)
3. $(128 \times 3) + (15 \times 6) + (8 \times 2) =$ (Answer: 490)
4. $(32 - 4) + (16 \times 2) - (11 - 10) =$ (Answer: 59)
5. $(83 \times 6) - (144 - 6) + (81 - 2) =$ (Answer: 522)
6. $96 - (8 \times 3) + (6 \times 7) =$ (Answer: 114)

Exercise 2.1

Problems for the calculator using $\boxed{\text{M+}}$ $\boxed{\text{M-}}$ $\boxed{\text{MRC}}$ or $\boxed{\text{RCM}}$.

1. A shopkeeper sold 87 apples on Thursday and three times as many on Friday.
   (a) How many apples were sold on Saturday if 537 were sold altogether over the three days?
   (b) Find the average number of apples sold each day.

2. There are 36 pear trees and three times as many apple trees in an orchard. The rest were plum trees. If there were 212 trees altogether, how many plum trees were there?

3. A forester planted 4 rows of trees with 68 in each row and 5 rows with 64 in each. If he had 700 trees altogether, find:
   (a) How many trees had he still to plant?
   (b) If he planted the remainder in 2 rows how many in each?

4. There were 618 people seated at a match. There were 7 times as many standing. How many short of 5000 were at the match?

5. A dealer sold 5 used cars at €1675 each and bought 3 other cars at €2500 each. How much did he gain on the transactions?

The use of the electronic calculator

Main Key Functions

(a) FCUT5/4   F CUT 5/4

Specifies the rounding system.

F: Floating decimal point system, which displays the value without rounding.
Cut: Cuts off the decimal to the specified* number of places.
5/4: Rounds off the decimal to the specified* number of places.

*Use the decimal place selector to specify the number of decimal places.

(b) 4 3 2 0 ADD₂   4 3 2 1 0 ADD₂   Decimal Place Selector

Specifies the number of decimal places for rounding.

4.3.2.1.0: Number of decimal places for the CUT and 5/4 setting of the rounding select
ADD_2: The 'add mode' automatically adds a decimal point and two decimal places
values, even if a decimal point is not input.

(c) GT Memory Switch

GT on/off

Setting GT memory switch to the 'on' position activates the grand total memory, wh
'off' position deactivates grand total memory.

(d)

$\boxed{-}$ = subtraction key

$\boxed{+}$ = addition key

$\boxed{\times}$ = multiplication key

$\boxed{\div}$ = division key

$\boxed{\%}$ = percentage key

$\boxed{\sqrt{}}$ = square root calculations

(e) Constant calculations
Input the number you want to use as a constant and then press one of the arithme
twice. This causes the 'k' indicator to appear on the display, indicating constant calcu

(f) Independent memory

$\boxed{M+}$ This key puts the number on the display into the memory. If there is a numbe
in the memory, it is added to it.

$\boxed{M-}$ This subtracts the number on display from the number in the memory.

6. A TV dealer sold 6 black-and-white sets at €128 each and 4 colour sets at €475 each. How much short of €3200 did he get?

(g) Grand total memory

 = adds the calculated result to grand total memory

GT recalls the value stored (accumulated) in grand total memory

AC Clears the grand total memory

Note: Grand total memory contents are cleared when power is switched off by the auto power off function.

(h) Correcting input errors

● To completely clear a value you have just input, press C .

● To shift a displayed value digit-by-digit to the right, press ▶ until you get to the digit you want to re-input from.

● If you press the wrong arithmetic operation key (+ , − , × , ÷), simply press correct key before inputting anything else.

(i) Clearing calculations

● To clear the calculator completely except for the independent memory, press AC .

● To clear the independent memory only, press MC .

(j) Euro currency conversion

● Euro Currency/Conversion Rate Key

Natl National currency key

 Conversion rate set key

Note: Pressing AC to clear the calculation memory does not clear independent memory or the conversion rate setting.

● To set a conversion rate

Example: 1 euro = IR£0.787564

$$0.$$

1. Press AC .
2. Hold down rate set for about two seconds and the currently set rate appears on the display.

3. Input the conversion rate and then press *rate set* to store it in memory.

EURO   RATE
 1   0.787564

€1 = £0.787564 (0.79 for usual use)
£1 = €1.269738 (1.27 for usual use)
£ to € ×1.27

You can check the currently set rate at any time by pressing $\boxed{AC}$ and then $\boxed{\text{Euro}}^{\text{RATE}}$.

The rate is retained in memory even when the calculator power is turned off by pressing off *or* by operation of auto power off.

Exercise 2.2

1. $872 \times 463 \times 472 =$
2. $963.4 \times 79.225 =$

3. $\dfrac{11.23 \times 7.64}{1.7 \times 3.63} =$

4. 19% of a sum of money is €152. What is the sum?
5. Find the value of $180 - (42.5\%$ of $180)$.
6. A number is increased by 25%. If the new number is 6840, what was the original number?
7. Calculate $7.37 + 18.825 - 13.374$.
8. The cost of a video is €250. The selling price is €320. Find the percentage profit.
9. $982 \times 763 \times 274 =$
10. $593.4 \times 82.9 \times 25 =$

11. $\dfrac{10.23 \times 7.64}{2.9 \times 4.67} =$

12. 13% of a sum of money is €79. What is the sum?
13. Find the value of $150 - (33.5\%$ of $150)$.
14. A number is increased by 20%. If the new number is 7320, what was the original number?
15. Calculate $8.34 + 15.285 - 17.437$.
16. The cost of a washing machine is €425. The selling price is €475. Find the percentage profit.
17. $782 \times 643 \times 274 =$
18. $693.4 \times 72.925 =$

19. $\dfrac{10.23 \times 7.64}{1.9 \times 4.67} =$

20. 14% of a sum of money is €77. What is the sum?
21. Find the value of $150 - (20\%$ of $150)$.
22. A number is increased by 20%. If the new number is 8460, what was the original number?
23. Calculate $6.34 + 15.23 - 19.62$.
24. The cost of a washing machine is €465. The selling price is €493. Find the percentage profit.

CHAPTER 3
Measurement and mensuration

In this chapter we will deal with:
— **the metric system, length, area, volume and mass (weight)**
— **imperial to metric conversion**
— **scale, ratio and proportion**
— **the unitary method of calculation**
— **calculations with time.**

THE METRIC SYSTEM

Nowadays the preferred measurement system is the metric system, also known as the SI system from the French Systeme International d'Unités (International System of Units). The metric system is based on the decimal system, i.e. fractions of units are $\frac{1}{10}$, $\frac{1}{100}$, $\frac{1}{1000}$ and multiples are 10, 100, 1 000.

Length

For length the unit of measurement is the metre (m).
Some important fractions and multiples of the metre are:

10 millimetres (mm) = 1 centimetre (cm)	**Most used**
10 cm = 1 decimetre (dm)	100 mm = 1 cm
10 dm = 1 m	100 cm = 1 000 mm = 1 m
1000 mm = 100 cm = 1 m	1 000 m = 1 km
10 m = 1 decametre (dam)	
10 dam = 1 hectometre (hm)	
10 hm = 1 kilometre (km)	
1000 m = 1 km	

Although the metre is the standard unit, it is not always the most useful. For example, kilometres make more sense for distances between towns and millimetres are better suited to measuring the thickness of cardboard.

Area

For area the basic unit is the square metre (m^2).

100 sq. millimetres (mm^2) = 1 sq. centimetre (cm^2)	**Most used**
100 cm^2 = 1 sq. decimetre (dm^2)	mm^2
100 dm^2 = 1 m^2	cm^2
1 000 000 mm^2 = 10 000 cm^2 = 1 m^2	m^2
100 m^2 = 1 are (a)	km^2
100 a = 1 hectare (ha)	
100 ha = 1 sq. kilometre (km^2)	
1 000 000 m^2 = 1 km^2	

Example 1

(a) How many millimetres are there in 8 decametres?

(b) Add 23 centimetres to 56 metres.

(c) Subtract 67 square metres from 5 ares.

Answer

(a) 8 dam = 80 m = 80 000 mm

(b) 56 m = 5600 cm
5600 cm + 23 cm = 5623 cm

(c) 5 a = 500 m^2
500 m^2 – 67 m^2 = 433 m^2

Calculation of area

The most important and frequently occurring shapes for which areas will have to be calculated are rectangles, triangles, circles and cylinders. Most shapes are made up of these elements.

Example 2

Rectangle – a quadrilateral (four-sided) figure with opposite sides equal and its four angles right angles.
The area of a rectangle is found by multiplying its length by its breadth, i.e.

Area = $l \times b$

Find the area of the rectangle shown below.

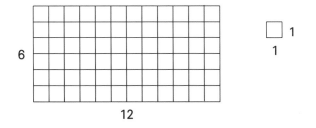

Answer

Area = $12 \times 6 = 72$ units

Example 3

Find the area of the shape below. All measurements are in metres.

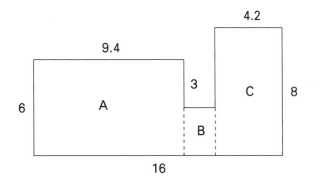

Answer

(a) Divide the shape into its component parts (as above).

(b) Find any unknown measurements.

(c) Calculate the area of each of the components.

(d) Add the areas together.

(b) Area A – No unknown measurements.
  Area B – Base = $16 - (9.4 + 4.2) = 16 - 13.6 = 2.4$ m
  Area C – No unknown measurements.

(c) Area A = $(6)(9.4) = 56.4$ m^2
  Area B = $(2.4)(3) = 7.2$ m^2
  Area C = $(4.2)(8) = 33.6$ m^2

(d) Total area = $56.4 + 7.2 + 33.6 = 97.2$ m^2.

Example 4

Find the tiled area around the swimming pool shown below. All measurements are in metres.

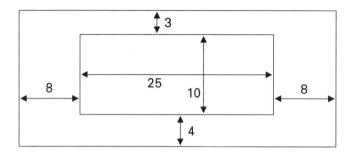

Answer

Take the area of the swimming pool from the total area.

Total area $= (3 + 4 + 10)(8 + 8 + 25) = 697$ m^2
Area of swimming pool $= (10)(25) = 250$ m^2
Tiled area $= 697 - 250 = 447$ m^2

Example 5

The diagram below shows the dimensions of a room. Find the area of the floor not covered by the carpet, if a border 40 centimetres wide is to be left.

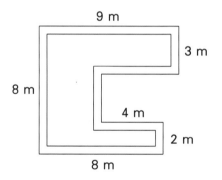

Answer

Area of room $= (8)(4) + (5)(3) + (4)(2) = 53$ m^2
Area of carpet $= (7.2)(3.2) + (5)(2.2) + (4)(1.2) = 38.84$ m^2
Area of floor not covered by carpet $= 53 - 38.84 = 14.16$ m^2

Example 6

Triangle – a three-sided figure.
The area of a triangle is half the base by the perpendicular height.

Area $= \frac{1}{2}b \times h$

Find the area of the triangle shown below.

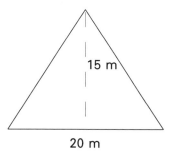

Answer

Area = $(\frac{1}{2})(20)(15) = 150$ m^2

Example 7

Circle – a circle is defined as the locus (location) of a point moving on a flat plane at a constant distance (the radius) from another, stationary point (the centre).
The circumference of a circle is a certain number of times larger than the diameter.

This number is called pi, $\pi = \frac{22}{7}$
Circumference = πd

This is approximated to 3.14, correct to two decimal places.
The area of a circle is pi times the radius squared, where the radius is equal to half the diameter.

Area = πr^2

Find the area of the circle below if the radius is 14 cm.

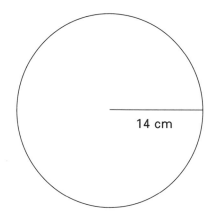

Answer

Area = $(\frac{22}{7})(14)^2 = 616$ cm^2

Example 8

Cylinder – a cylinder consists of two circles and a curved surface. If the curved surface was flattened out it would form a rectangle. The area of the cylinder is therefore the sum of the areas of the two circles and the area of the rectangle, which is equal to the circumference of the circles multiplied by the height of the cylinder.

$$\text{Area} = 2\pi r^2 + 2\pi rh = 2\pi r(r+h)$$

Find the area of the cylinder shown below.

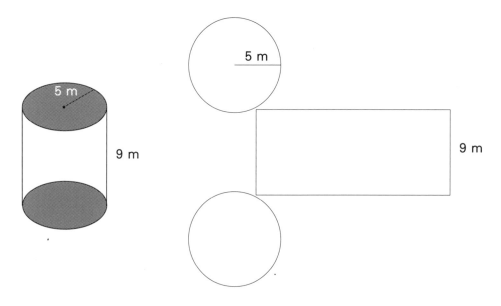

Answer

$$\text{Area} = 2(\tfrac{22}{7})(5)(5+9) = 2(\tfrac{22}{7})(5)(14) = 440 \text{ m}^2$$

Example 9

You are working for a local garden centre which wants to convert part of its lawn to a shrubbery. The lawn is in two sections divided by a path, as shown below. As a first step they have asked you to calculate the area of each section of the lawn.

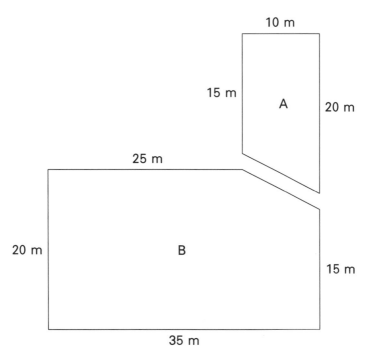

Answer

Area A = $(20)(10) - \frac{1}{2}(10)(5) = 200 - 25 = 175$ m^2
Area B $(35)(20) - \frac{1}{2}(10)(5) = 675$ m^2

Example 10

Find the unshaded area in the diagram below. The radius of each circle is 2.5 cm.

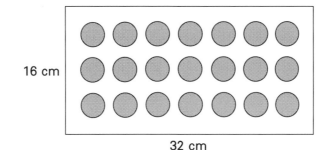

Answer

Since the circles are of the same radius, the area of 21 of these circles is simply $21(\pi r^2) =$
$21(3.14)(2.5)(2.5) = 412.125$ cm^2

Area of rectangle $= (16)(32) = 512$ cm^2
Unshaded area $= 512 - 412.125 = 99.875$ cm

Example 11

How many *complete* circles of radius 3 cm can be cut from the rectangle shown below?

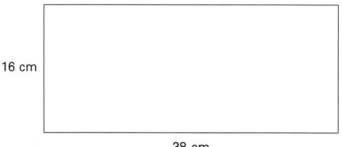

16 cm

38 cm

Answer

Unless the pieces can be joined back together again, the number of circles must equal the
number of squares with the same size sides as the diameter (as shown above).
Each circle has a diameter of 6 cm.

The number of circles along the length $= \frac{38}{6} = 6$ complete circles.
The number of circles down the side $= \frac{16}{6} = 2$ complete circles.
The total number of circles $= (6)(2) = 12$ circles.

Exercise 3.1

1. Convert each of the following to millimetres.
    (a) 46 cm
    (b) 4 dm
    (c) 4 cm
    (d) 6 m
    (e) 8.5 dm

2. Convert each of the following to centimetres.
    (a) 6 dm
    (b) 455 mm
    (c) 7 dam
    (d) 3 m
    (e) 7.2 dm

3. Convert each of the following to metres.
    (a) 490 cm
    (b) 55 dm
    (c) 6 dm
    (d) 5600 mm
    (e) 3 km
    (f) 4 hm

4. How many kilometres in 78 000 dam?

5. Convert each of the following to square millimetres.
    (a) 43 cm^2
    (b) 5.2 m^2
    (c) 34 dm^2

6. Convert each of the following to square centimetres.
    (a) 3200 mm^2
    (b) 35 m^2
    (c) 45 dm^2

7. Convert each of the following to square metres.
    (a) 49 ha
    (b) 5 km^2
    (c) 2 500 000 mm^2
    (d) 97 a
    (e) 3 560 dm^2
    (f) 47 000 cm^2

8. I am on a journey from Kilkenny to Carlow. If Kilkenny is 40 km from Carlow and I have already travelled 4000 m, how much further do I have to go, in kilometres?

9. Find the area of each of the following rectangles.
   (a) $b = 5$ cm, $h = 6$ cm
   (b) $b = 4$ m, $h = 8$ m
   (c) $b = 20$ dam, $h = 5$ dam
   (d) $b = 10$ mm, $h = 3$ mm

10. Find the area of each of the following shapes.

(a)

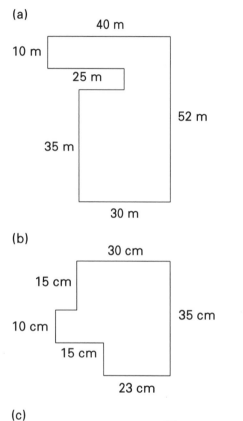

(b)

(c)

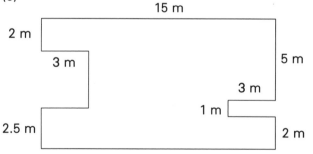

11. For each of the following shapes, calculate the area of the border, if in each case it is 50 cm wide.

(a)

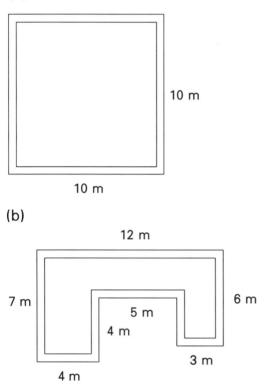

10 m

10 m

(b)

12 m

7 m

6 m

5 m

4 m

3 m

4 m

12. (a) Find the floor area of the following room.

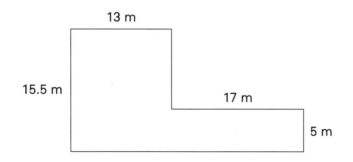

13 m

15.5 m

17 m

5 m

(b) If the walls are 2.8 metres high and 12 square metres are allowed for windows and doors, find the area of the walls.

13. Find the area of each of the following triangles.
   (a) $b = 8$ cm, $h = 12$ cm
   (b) $b = 6$ mm, $h = 7$ mm
   (c) $b = 5$ m, $h = 2$ m
   (d) $b = 30$ mm, $h = 2$ cm
   (e) $b = 7$ cm, $h = 15$ cm

14. Find the area of each of the following circles.
    (a) $r = 7$ cm
    (b) $r = 14$ m
    (c) $r = 119$ mm
    (d) $r = 35$ cm
    (e) $r = 10.5$ dam
    (f) $d = 5.25$ m

15. Find the surface area of each of the following cylinders.
    (a) $r = 14$ cm, $h = 34$ cm
    (b) $r = 21$ m, $h = 10$ m
    (c) $r = 10.5$ mm, $h = 20$ mm
    (d) $d = 42$ cm, $h = 42$ cm
    (e) $r = 70$ cm, $h = 1$ m
    (f) $d = 63$ cm, $h = 1.2$ m

16. Find the area of the garden shown below.

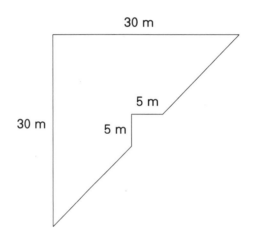

17. (a) How many complete circles of radius 7 cm can be cut from a square piece of material of side 70 cm?
    (b) What is the area of material that is wasted, i.e. unusable?

18. Your employers have a small rectangular park, measuring 20 m by 30 m. It has a circular flower bed measuring 7 m in diameter and two triangular flower beds, each of height 8 m and base 6 m. The remaining area is a lawn.
    Calculate:

    (a) the total area of the flower beds
    (b) the area of the lawn.

Volume and capacity

For volume the standard unit is the cubic metre, m^3.

1000 cubic millimetres (mm^3) = 1 cubic centimetre (cm^3)
1000 cm^3 = 1 cubic decimetre (dm^3)
1000 dm^3 = 1 cubic metre
1 000 000 cm^3 = 1 m^3

Most used
1000 mm^3 = 1 cm^3
1000 000 cm^3 = 1 m^3

For capacity the standard unit is the litre, l.

10 millilitres (ml) = 1 centilitre (cl)
10 cl = 1 decilitre (dl)
10 dl = 1 litre
1000 ml = 1 l
10 l = 1 decalitre (dal)
10 dal = 1 hectolitre (hl)
1000 cm^3 = 1 l
1 m^3 = 1000 l

Most used
1000 ml = 1 l
1000 cm^3 = 1 l
1 m^3 = 1000 l

Example 12

Cuboid (box) – the volume of a cuboid is the length by the breadth by the height.

Volume = $l \times b \times h$

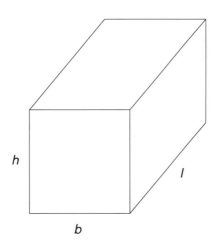

If the height of a cuboid is 34 m, the base is 23 m and the length is 56 m what is its volume?

Answer

Volume = (56)(23)(34) = 43 792 m^3

Example 13

Cylinder – the volume of the cuboid is the area of the base multiplied by the height. We can also apply this to a cylinder, so the volume of a cylinder is pi times the radius squared multiplied by the height.

Volume = $\pi r^2 h$

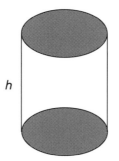

If the radius of a cylinder is 45 cm and the height is 78 cm, what is the volume?

Answer

Volume = $\pi r^2 h = (3.14)(45)^2(78) = 495\ 963$ cm³

Example 14

Sphere (ball) – the volume of a sphere is the radius cubed multiplied by four-thirds pi.

Volume = $\frac{4}{3}\pi r^3$

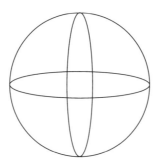

Find the volume of a sphere of radius 7 m.

Answer

Volume = $\frac{4}{3}\pi r^3 = (\frac{4}{3})(\frac{22}{7})(7)^3 = 65.33$ m³

Example 15

Hemisphere (half a sphere) – the volume of a hemisphere is half that of a sphere.

Volume $= \frac{2}{3}\pi r^3$

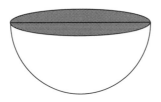

Find the volume of a hemisphere of radius 21 cm.

Answer

Volume $= \frac{2}{3}\pi r^3 = (\frac{2}{3})(\frac{22}{7})(21)^3 = 19\ 404$ cm^3

Example 16

Cone – the volume of a cone is pi times the radius of the base squared multiplied by the height and divided by three.

Volume $= 1/3\pi r^2 h$

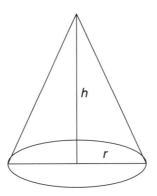

Find the volume of a cone of radius 10 cm and height 21 cm.

Answer

Volume $= \frac{1}{3}\pi r^2 h = (\frac{1}{3})(\frac{22}{7})(10)^2(21) = 2200$ cm^3

Example 17

(a) Find the volume of a silo consisting of a cylinder with a cone on top, as shown below. The total height is 25 m with the cylinder making up 80% of the height. The radius of the cylinder is 7.5 m.

(b) If the silo is filled to a height of 18 m, how many litres is it holding?

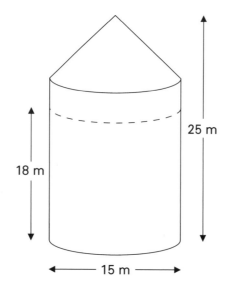

Answer

(a) 80% of 25 m = 20 m

The height of the cylinder = h_1 = 20 m

Therefore the height of the cone = h_2 = 5 m

Volume of cylinder = $V_1 = \pi r^2 h = 3.14(7.5)^2(20) = 3532.5$ m^3

Volume of cone = $V_2 = \frac{1}{3}\pi r^2 h = \frac{1}{3}(3.14)(7.5)^2(5) = 294.375$ m^3

Total volume = 3532.5 m^3 + 294.375 m^3 = 3826.875 m^3

(b) Total volume used = $\pi r^2 h = (3.14)(7.5)^2(18) = 3179.25$ m^3

1 m^3 = 1000 l

Therefore 3179.25 m^3 = 3 179 250 l

Example 18

How many cylindrical cans of radius 3 cm and height 12 cm can be packed in a box 37 cm high, 20 cm wide and 60 cm long?

Answer

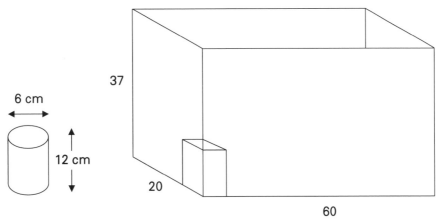

Each cylinder will effectively take up the space of a cuboid 12 cm high, 6 cm long and 6 cm wide.

(a) Divide the height of the box by 12 cm.
$\frac{37}{12} = 3.083\ldots$
3 full cans

(b) Divide the width by 6 cm
$\frac{20}{6} = 3.3.\ldots$
3 full cans

(c) Divide the length by 6 cm
$\frac{60}{6} = 10$
10 full cans

Therefore the total number of cans = (3)(3)(10) = 90 cans.

Example 19

A litre of milk is in a carton which is 6 cm wide and 9 cm long. What is the height of the carton correct to one decimal place?

Answer

$$1 \text{ litre} = 1000 \text{ cm}^3$$
$$l \times b \times h = 1000 \text{ cm}^3$$
$$6 \times 9 \times h = 1000 \text{ cm}^3$$
$$54 \times h = 1000 \text{ cm}^3$$
$$h = \frac{1000}{54}$$
$$h = 18.5 \text{ cm}$$

Mass (Weight)

The standard unit of weight is the gramme or gram (g).

10 milligrams (mg) = 1 centigram (cg)   **Most used**
10 centigrams = 1 decigram (dg)   1000 mg = 1 g
10 dg = 1 gram (g)   1000 g = 1 kg
1000 mg = 1 g   1000 kg = 1 tonne
10 g = 1 decagram (dag)
10 dag = 1 hectogram (hg)
10 hg = 1 kilogram (kg)
1000 g = 1 kg
1000 kg = 1 tonne (t)

Density

When physicists talk about density they mean mass per unit volume (volumetric density), but equally important is areal density, i.e. per unit area. An example of areal density would be crowd/population density, number of people per unit area.

Example 20

For safety purposes no more than 20 000 people are to be allowed to attend a concert which is being held in your area. If the crowd density at the concert, given maximum attendance, is 4 people per square metre, what is the area the crowd occupies?

Answer

$\frac{20\,000}{4} = 5000$ m^2

Example 21

You are working for a local firm. On their property they have a park measuring 20 m by 38 m with two circular flower beds each with a diameter of 8 metres and a diamond-shaped flower bed with dimensions as shown below.

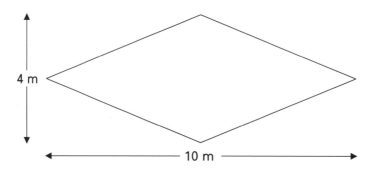

The park was a recent development and the whole area (excluding the flower beds) is to be sown with grass at 1 kg per 50 m^2. What weight of grass-seed, to the nearest kilogram, should be sown?

Answer

Area of park = $l \times b = 20 \times 38 = 760 \text{ m}^2$
Area of one circular flower bed = $\pi r^2 = (3.14)(4)^2 = 50.24 \text{ m}^2$
Area of two circular flower beds = $50.24 \times 2 = 100.48 \text{ m}^2$

The diamond shaped flower bed can be divided into two triangular shapes of equal area, as shown below.

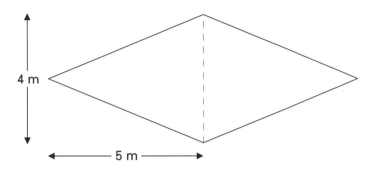

Area of the diamond = $2\,(\frac{1}{2} \times b \times h) = 2\,(\frac{1}{2} \times 4 \times 5) = 20 \text{ m}^2$
Total area of flower beds = $100.48 + 20 = 120.48 \text{ m}^2$
Total area of lawn = $760 - 120.48 = 639.52 \text{ m}^2$
Quantity of seed = $\frac{639.52}{50} = 12.790 \text{ kg}$
Answer = 13 kg

Example 22

A liquid has a volumetric density of 1.2 kg/m³. It is stored in containers which each have a capacity of 1 litre. What is the weight of liquid in each container?

Answer

1 litre = $1/1000 \text{ m}^3$
Weight = density multiplied by volume = $(1.2)(\frac{1}{1000}) = 0.0012 \text{ kg} = 1.2 \text{ g.}$

Exercise 3.2

1. (a) How many cm³ are there in 3.56 m³?
   (b) What is 3500 m³ in cubic centimetres?
   (c) Subtract 44 394 cm³ from 5.92 m³.
   (d) Add 40 724 000 cm³ to 421 m³.
   (e) How many litres are there in 2.92 m³?
   (f) How many cubic cm are there in 49 litres?

2. Find the volume of each of the following cuboids.

(a)

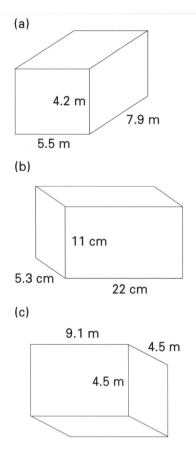

4.2 m

7.9 m

5.5 m

(b)

11 cm

5.3 cm

22 cm

(c)

9.1 m

4.5 m

4.5 m

3. A rectangular oil tank has dimensions 3 m long, 1.49 m wide and 2.1 m high. How many litres of oil can it hold? How many litres would it contain if it were only 65% full?

4. Find the volume of each of the following cylinders

(a)

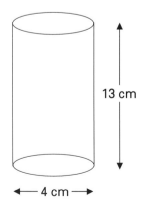

13 cm

←— 4 cm —→

(b)

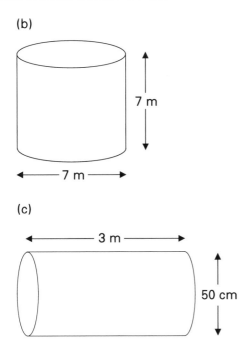

7 m

7 m

(c)

3 m

50 cm

5. What is the volume of the wall of the pipe?

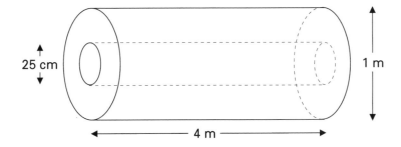

25 cm

1 m

4 m

6. Find the volume of each of the following shapes.

(a)

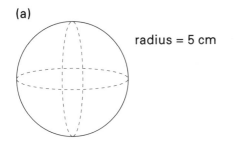

radius = 5 cm

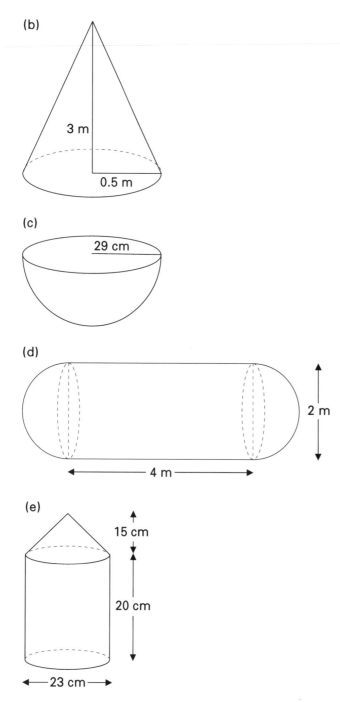

(b)

3 m

0.5 m

(c)

29 cm

(d)

2 m

4 m

(e)

15 cm

20 cm

23 cm

7. A storage tank consisting of a cylinder with two hemispherical ends is shown below. It has a total length of 30 m and can be filled at a rate of 5000 l per minute. After how many minutes will it be 50% full?

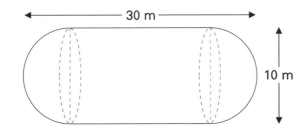

8. You are working for Jones Ltd. They recently acquired new premises and are currently landscaping the area around the building, as shown below. You are required to:
   (a) Find the total area to be landscaped.
   (b) Find the area which will be flower beds.
   (c) Find the area which will be a lawn.
   (d) Find the amount of grass seed, to the nearest kilogram, which is to be purchased if the amount required is 1 kg per 50 m².
   (e) Find the cost of the grass seed if it costs €2.00 per kilogram.

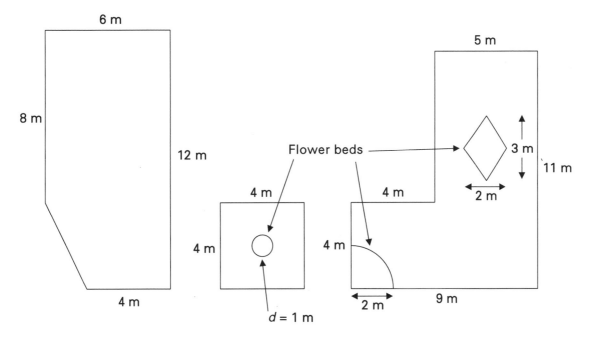

9. You were involved in conducting a survey on the traffic in Dublin. During your study you found that the density of occupants was 1.3 people per car. In a queue of cars at some traffic lights you counted 23 cars. Given the density of occupants you found, how many people were stuck at the traffic lights, to the next whole number?

IMPERIAL TO METRIC CONVERSION

Although Ireland has officially adopted the metric system many people still use the British or imperial system of measurement. Therefore, it is useful to be able to convert to metric measurements, as imperial measurements may be supplied.

Length

1 inch (1") = 25.4 mm = 2.54 cm
1 foot (1') = 12 inches = 0.305 m
1 yard = 3 feet = 0.915 m
1 mile = 1.61 km ($\approx \frac{8}{5}$ km)

NB: 1 inch = 2.54 cm
39.4 inches = 1 metre
ft to metres × 12 ÷ 39.4

Area

1 sq. inch = 6.39 cm^2
1 sq. foot = 0.093 m^2
1 sq. yard = 0.836 m^2
1 acre = 0.405 hectares = 40.5 ares

Volume

1 cu. inch = 16.235 cm^3
1 cu. foot = 0.002 m^3
1 cu. yard = 0.765 m^3

Capacity

1 pint = 0.568 litre
1 gallon = 4.55 litre
1 litre = 1.76 pints

1 l = 1.76 pints ($1\frac{3}{4}$)
500 ml = $\frac{1}{2}$ l = $\frac{7}{8}$ pt

Mass (weight)

1 ounce (oz) = 28.37 g
1 pound (lb) = 0.454 kg
1 ton (Imperial) = 1.016 tonnes (metric)

1 lb = 0.454 kg

Exercise 3.3

1. How many litres equal 7 pints?

2. How many millilitres are there in 3.5 gallons?

3. How many centimetres equal 37 inches?

4. How many centimetres are there in 4 feet 7 inches?

5. What is 5 feet 10 inches in metres?

6. What is 5 yards, 2 feet and 4 inches in metres?

7. What is $50\frac{3}{4}$ miles in kilometres?

8. If a farmer has a 400 acre farm, how many ares does he have?

9. If your garden measures 190 square yards, how many m^2 is it?

10. How many sq. metres equal 10 sq. feet?

11. How many sq. centimetres equal 5.5 sq. inches?

12. How many cubic centimetres equal 4 cubic feet?

13. How many grams equal 7 ounces?

14. How many kilograms equal 5 pounds 6 ounces?

15. You have found the area of your new lawn to be 400 m^2 and want to sow it with grass. Grass seed costs €2 per lb and you require 1 kg per 50 m^2. How much will it cost you?

RATIO

Ratio expresses the relationship between one quantity and another in its lowest form, where both quantities represent values of the same thing.
The units must be the same. For example, you cannot combine metres and centimetres, you must convert them so they are in the same units. The ratio itself has *no* units.

Example 23

Two people jointly buy a Lotto ticket. One buys 2 lines and the other 3 lines. They win €7 500. They divide the money in the ration 2 is to 3 (written 2 : 3). There are 5 lines. Divide €7 500 by 5 to get the value of each line. Multiply the answer by 2 and by 3.

$7\ 500 \div 5 = 1\ 500$

One person gets €1 500 × 2 = €3 000
The other gets €1 500 × 3 = €4 500

As a fraction:

One gets $\frac{2}{5}$ of the money
The other gets $\frac{3}{5}$ of the money

Example 24

A farmer buys a bag of grain called 10 : 10 : 20. The bag contains 3 different substances divided in this ratio
In its lowest form 10 : 10 : 20 = 1 : 1 : 2.
Fraction of each: $\frac{1}{4}$ $\frac{1}{4}$ $\frac{2}{4}$ of the full amount.

PROPORTION

This is the relationship between four, or more numbers (so long as there is an even number), grouped in twos, where the ratio of the first group equals the ratio of the second, third etc. groups.

Example 25

First group: 3, 15
Second group: 1, 5

These two sets are in *direct proportion* to each other, i.e. $\frac{3}{15} = \frac{1}{5}$

Cross-multiplying: $\frac{3}{15} \bowtie \frac{1}{5}$
3(5) = 1(15)
15 = 15

Cross-multiplying is a useful tool for finding unknown quantities.

Example 26

First group: 2, 3
Second group: x, 15

Find x.

Answer

$\frac{2}{3} = \frac{x}{15}$
2(15) = 3(x)
30 = 3x
$x = \frac{30}{3} = 10$

Example 27

If a bus travels 111 km in 1.5 hours how far would it go in 2 hours at the same speed?

Answer

$$\frac{111}{1\frac{1}{2}} = \frac{x}{2}$$

$$\frac{222}{3} = \frac{x}{2}$$

$$3x = 444$$

$$x = \frac{444}{3} = 148 \text{ km}$$

Unitary method

The above example could also have been solved by the unitary method, i.e. by reasoning it out. Work out how far the bus goes in 1 hour, then find the answer for 2 hours.

$$1 \text{ hr} = \frac{111}{1\frac{1}{2}} = \frac{222}{3} = 74$$

in 2 hrs $74 \times 2 = 148$ km

Example 28

Use:

(a) proportion

(b) the unitary method

to find the unknown quantity, x.
If 10 copies cost €1.30, how much would 12 copies cost?

Answer

(a) $\frac{10}{12} = \frac{1.30}{x}$
$\quad 10x = (1.30)(12)$
$\quad x = \frac{15.60}{10}$
$\quad x = €1.56$

(b) 10 copies cost €1.30
$\quad$ 1 copy costs $\frac{1.30}{10} = €0.13$
$\quad$ 12 copies cost $(0.13)(12) = €1.56$

Inverse proportion

So far we have only dealt with *direct proportion*, i.e. as one quantity increases so does the other. But sometimes an increase in one quantity produces a reduction in the other; this is known as *inverse proportion*.

Example 29

If it takes a car 4 hours to complete a journey at 80 km/h, how long will the same journey take at 100 km/h?

Answer

$$4 \text{ hrs at } 800 \text{ km/h} = 320 \text{ km}$$
$$\text{at } 100 \text{ km/h} = \tfrac{320}{100} = 3.2 \text{ hrs}$$
$$= 3 \text{ hrs } 12 \text{ mins}$$

SCALE

One of the most frequent uses of ratio and proportion is in scaling. For example, the scale appears on all maps, where the distances are scaled down to make them easier to use (can you imagine a full size map of Ireland?). It is also used for making models which have the same proportions as the actual object. The relationships between different measurements remain the same, but the measurements themselves are made smaller or larger.

Example 30

The distance between Coleraine and Portstewart is 2.5 cm on a map. If the scale is 1 : 250 000, what is the actual distance between these towns in kilometres?

Answer

$$1 : 250\,000$$
$$2.5 : x$$

Cross-multiply

$$x = (2.5)\,(250\,000)$$
$$x = 625\,000 \text{ cm} = 6.25 \text{ km}$$

Example 31

A bus is 25 m long with wheels of diameter 0.9 m. If a model of the bus is 200 cm long, what is the diameter of the wheels on the model?

Answer

Ratio of model to bus

$$200 \text{ cm} : 25 \text{ m}$$
$$\equiv 200 \text{ cm} : 2500 \text{ cm}$$
$$\equiv 2 : 25$$
$$\equiv 1 : 12.5$$
$$1 : 12.5$$
$$x : 90$$

Cross-multiply

$$(12.5)(x) = 90$$
$$x = \tfrac{90}{12.5} = 7.2 \text{ cm}$$

Example 32

A component of a machine, which has an overall height of 18 mm, is to be scaled up in a model for presentation purposes. A cylindrical part of the component has a diameter of 3 mm and a height of 4 mm. If the overall height of the model is 36 cm, what are the measurements of the cylindrical part of the model?

Answer

18 mm : 36 cm
$\equiv$ 18 mm: 360 mm
$\equiv$ 1 : 20

Diameter

1 : 20
3 : x
x = 60 mm = 6 cm

Height

1 : 20
4 : x
x = 80 mm = 8 cm

Exercise 3.4

1. €50 is to be divided between Mary, Helen, Liam and Alan in the ratio 2 : 4 : 2 : 2. How much does each person get?

2. €690 is to be divided between John, Paul, David, Elaine and Gavin in the ratio 3 : 5 : 2 : 6 : 4. How much does each person get?

3. Divide €300 in such a way that Olive gets three times as much as Anne and half as much as Suzanne.

4. A chemical mixture is made up of three compounds in the ratio 6 : 12 : 7. What is the weight of each compound in a mixture weighing 2392 kg?

5. What is the ratio of €12.50 to €9.30?

6. What is the ratio of 5 m to 5 cm?

7. What is the ratio of 15 kg to 720 kg?

8. If two circles have areas 120 736 cm^2 and 616 cm^2 respectively, what is the proportion of:
   (a) their areas
   (b) their radii.

9. Express €1.19 and €35.70 as:
   (a) a proportion in its lowest terms
   (b) a decimal.

10. Express as a decimal the proportion of 2197 m to 37 349 m .

For questions 11–14, find x.

11. $\frac{4}{x} = \frac{12}{15}$

12. $\frac{7}{9} = \frac{63}{x}$

13. $\frac{3}{7} = \frac{x}{119}$

14. $\frac{4}{11} = \frac{16}{x}$

15. If a car travels 90 km in 45 minutes, how far will it travel in $3\frac{1}{2}$ hours?

16. If a worker does 210 units in 25 minutes, how many will be done in an hour?

17. The distance between Enniskerry and Stepaside measures 8.1 cm on a map. How far is it to the nearest kilometre if the scale is 1 : 100 000?

18. If the Rathmines road from the canal to the junction at Castlewood Avenue is 4.1 cm on a map and the scale of the map is 1:20 000, how long is that road?

19. For presentation purposes, a model of a component has to be scaled up. The component has an overall height of 13.3 mm. The overall height of the model is 27.93 cm.
    (a) What is the proportion of model height to component height?
    (b) For part A of the component the measurements are 2.3 mm and 4.2 mm. What is the size of the corresponding part in the model?

20. The height of a building is 20 m. In a model its height is 25 cm. If the length of one wall is 13 m, what is the corresponding length in the model?

TIME

For business one needs to be able to perform calculations in both the 12 hour and 24 hour clocks and to be able to convert quickly from one to the other.

12 hour clock	1 am	2 am	3 am	4 am	5am	6 am	7 am	8 am	9 am	10 am	11 am	12 md
24 hour clock	01.00	02.00	03.00	04.00	05.00	06.00	07.00	08.00	09.00	10.00	11.00	12.00

12 hour clock	1 pm	2 pm	3 pm	4 pm	5 pm	6 pm	7 pm	8 pm	9 pm	10 pm	11 pm	12 mn
24 hour clock	13.00	14.00	15.00	16.00	17.00	18.00	19.00	20.00	21.00	22.00	23.00	00.00

Example 33

You wish to travel to Castlebar from Athy by bus. The first leg of your journey takes you 1 hour 15 minutes. You then have to wait 25 minutes for the bus to Castlebar, and this bus takes 4 hours 22 minutes to arrive at its destination.

Remember there are 60 seconds in 1 minute and 60 minutes in 1 hour.

(a) How long does your journey take you?

(b) If you start at 9.16 am what is your arrival time? Give both 12 and 24 hour clock times.

Answer

(a) hours minutes

1	15
+	25
+4	22

| 5 | 62 = 6 02 |

6 hours 2 minutes

(b) hours minutes

9	16
+6	02

| 15 | 18 |

in the 24 hour clock: 15.18
in the 12 hour clock: 3.18 pm

Example 34

Of a 4 hour 39 minute journey 47 minutes were due to stoppages. What amount of time was spent travelling and what was the departure time if the arrival time was 16.27?

Answer

hours	minutes		hours	minutes
4	39		3	99
−	47	→	−	47
			3	52

3 hours 52 minutes are spent travelling

hours	minutes		hours	minutes
16	27		15	87
−4	39	→	−4	39
			11	48

The journey began at 11.48 or 11.48 am.

Exercise 3.5

1. What is 4.10 pm in the 24 hour clock?

2. What is 2.10 am in the 24 hour clock?

3. What is 17.19 in the 12 hour clock?

4. What is 03.49 in the 12 hour clock?

5. You are journeying to New York by plane. If you leave at 9.15 am and fly direct the journey takes you 6 hours. What time will you arrive at? (Note: New York is 5 hours behind Ireland).

6. You start work at 9 am, you have a 15 minute break at 11 am, an hour for lunch at 1 pm and another 15 minute break at 3 pm. You finish at 4.30 pm. How many hours did you actually work?

7. A train journey takes you 5 hours to complete including waiting 47 minutes for a change of train. If you arrive at 1.28 pm what time did you start at and for how long were you actually travelling?

CHAPTER 4
Personal finance

In this chapter we will deal with:
— **household budget, including definitions of:**
   surplus
   deficit
   accruals
   current expenditure
   capital expenditure
   planned savings
— **household budget layout**
— **opening/closing cash**
— **comparison of budgeted income/expenditure with the actual**
— **exercises on estimating income/expenditure/costs and completing household/personal budgets.**

HOUSEHOLD BUDGET

You must have control over your money and in order to do that, you must have a plan. This type of plan is called a *budget*. A budget is devised by *estimating* income and *estimating* expenditure.

The difference between estimated income and estimated expenditure is either a *surplus* or a *deficit*. If there is no difference then there is *break-even*.

Surplus

This occurs when the estimated income is greater than the estimated expenditure.

Deficit

When the estimated expenditure is *greater* than the estimated income there is a deficit. To finance a deficit you may have to:

(1) alter your spending habits

(2) use some of your savings

(3) take out a short-term loan (overdraft).

Accruals

These are items which are paid for after you use them. The telephone bill and the electricity bill are examples of accruals. The household budget should estimate the amount due on these.

Current expenditure

Spending on day-to-day purchases is called current expenditure. For example, buying groceries, petrol or the newspaper.

Capital expenditure

Spending on consumer durables, such as a car, dishwasher etc. is called capital expenditure.

Planned savings

Saving means putting aside some income and spending it at a future date. It is important to plan savings, i.e. to plan to put aside a certain sum of money each week/month.

HOUSEHOLD BUDGET LAYOUT

Example 1: Mary's weekly budget

	Monday €	Tuesday €	Wednesday €	Thursday €	Friday €	Saturday €	Sunday €	Total for week €
Income	7	7	7	7	7	20	–	55
Expenditure	5	5	5	5	7	9	8	44
Savings	2	2	2	2	–	3	–	11

Mary has prepared this budget for a week. She is a student who gets money from her parents. Mary estimates that her *total income* for the week will be €55 and it will be received in various amounts on every day except Sunday. The *total expenditure* will be €45, which will be spent over the week. €11 is expected to be *saved* on Friday.

Note 1: Please note when preparing a budget that *under the heading income* you should include the income you expect to receive, e.g. wages, child benefit, interest on savings etc.
Note 2: *Under the heading expenditure* you should include your estimated *fixed, irregular and discretionary expenditure.*

Fixed expenditure

This is an expenditure which is *fixed in amount* and paid at *fixed times*. It includes: house mortgage or rent; loan repayments; insurance – life, medical, house, contents and car; car tax; TV licence.

Irregular expenditure

This is expenditure which *varies with use* and is paid at *different times* during the year. It includes: housekeeping costs; electricity; telephone; fuel; education; car expenses such as petrol and repairs.

Discretionary expenditure

This is expenditure which varies with the needs, likes and hobbies of people. It is *paid at different times* during the year. It includes: entertainment; holidays; donations; birthday presents; house decoration; car and furniture changes.

Note: *Under the heading savings*, you should include *all your estimated savings.*

Having completed the budget in the above way, you would then be in a position to match your estimated income with your estimated expenditure and savings.

Example 2: Six-month budget summary

	January €	February €	March €	April €	May €	June €	Total for 6 months €
(1) Total Income	600	600	800	800	800	800	4400
(2) Total Expenditure	500	700	500	800	650	810	3960
(1 − 2) Net Cash surplus or deficit	100	−100	300	–	150	−10	440

In January, March and May estimated income is greater than estimated expenditure therefore there is a *net cash surplus* in these months. In February and June estimated income is less than estimated expenditure, therefore there is a *net cash deficit* in these months. In April estimated income equals estimated expenditure, therefore there is *no net cash* – this is a break-even situation. Looking at the overall period of six months there is a *net surplus* of €440.

Note: Surplus is when income exceeds (>) expenditure. Deficit is when income is less than (<) expenditure.

Opening and closing cash positions

The *opening cash* position shows 'the amount of cash, if any, a person has starting off'.
The *closing cash* position is obtained by 'adding the net cash to the opening cash'.

Example 3: Six-month budget summary

	January €	February €	March €	April €	May €	June €	Total for 6 months €
(1) Total Income	600	600	800	800	800	800	4400
(2) Total Expenditure	500	700	500	800	650	810	3960
(3) Net cash (1 – 2)	100	–100	300	–	150	–10	440
(4) Opening cash	100	200	100	400	400	550	100
Closing cash (3 + 4)	200	100	400	400	550	540	540

Note: The closing cash position is obtained by 'adding the net cash to the opening cash'. The closing cash for one month is the opening cash for the next month.

Example 4: Question

Prepare a household budget for the Briody family for the first six months of 1997, using the following information.

Expected income

Mary Briody expects to earn €1000 net per month in January, February and March. In April, May and June she expects to earn €1200 net per month.
Peter Briody expects to earn €800 net per month in January, February, March and April. In May and June, he expects to earn €900 net per month.
The family expect to receive child benefit of €150 per month.

Expected expenditure

They expect to spend the following:

> Car loan repayment per month €300.
> House mortgage €400 per month.
> Annual car insurance €600 in January.
> House insurance €170 in January
> Annual car tax €100 in March.
> Telephone bill €100 in January, March and May.
> ESB bill €60 in February, April and June.
> Groceries per month €200
> Donations to charity: €40 in January, €10 in February, €30 in April, €20 in June.
> Entertainment: €150 in January, €80 in February, €80 in March, €50 in April, €60 in May, €50 in June.

The Briody family have *opening cash* of €100.

Answer

Household budget for the Briody family for the first six months of 1997

Income	January €	February €	March €	April €	May €	June €	Total €
Mary Briody wages	1000	1000	1000	1200	1200	1200	6600
Peter Briody wages	800	800	800	800	900	900	5000
Child benefit	150	150	150	150	150	150	900
1 Total income	1 950	1 950	1 950	2 150	2 250	2 250	12 500
Expenditure							
Fixed							
Car loan repayments	300	300	300	300	300	300	1800
Annual car insurance	600	–	–	–	–	–	600
House insurance	170	–	–	–	–	–	170
Mortgage	400	400	400	400	400	400	2400
Annual car tax	–	–	100	–	–	–	100
2 Subtotal	1 470	700	800	700	700	700	5070
Irregular							
Telephone bill	100	–	100	–	100	–	300
ESB bill	–	60	–	60	–	60	180
Groceries	200	200	200	200	200	200	1200
3 Subtotal	300	260	300	260	300	260	1680
Discretionary							
Donations	40	10	–	30	–	20	100
Entertainment	150	80	80	50	60	50	470
4 Subtotal	190	90	80	80	60	70	570
5 Total expenditure (2 + 3 + 4)	1960	1050	1180	1040	1060	1030	7320
6 Net cash (1 – 5)	(10)	900	770	1110	1190	1220	5180
7 Opening Cash	100	90	990	1760	2870	4060	100
Closing cash (6+7)	90	990	1 760	2 870	4060	5280	5280

Note:
(1) Figures in brackets such as (10) mean a deficit.
(2) Closing cash in one month is the opening cash for the next month.

Comparisons

By comparing the actual and the budgeted income and expenditure, you may be able to spot trends and avoid mistakes in the next budget. Maybe you can spot some trends in the following example.

Comparison of actual income/expenditure with estimated income/expenditure for the Briody family for first six months of 1997

Income	Budget total €	Actual total €
Mary Briody wages	6660	6600
Peter Briody wages	5000	5000
Child benefit	900	700
1 Total income	12 500	12 300
Expenditure		
Fixed		
Car loan repayments	1800	1800
Annual car insurance	600	700
House insurance	170	200
Mortgage	2400	2300
Annual car tax	100	120
2 Subtotal	5070	5120
Irregular		
Telephone bill	300	500
ESB bill	180	250
Groceries	1200	2000
3 Subtotal	1680	2750
Discretionary		
Donations	100	100
Entertainment	470	460
4 Subtotal	570	560
5 Total expenditure (2+3+4)	7320	8430
6 Net cash (1–5)	5180	3870
7 Opening cash	100	100
Closing cash (6 + 7)	5280	4970

Exercise 4.1

1. (a) Estimate the future income of the following employees who are expecting a 3% increase in their monthly wages.
   Mary earns €800 per month,
   June earns €1200 per month,
   James earns €1000 per month.
   (b) Estimate how much interest each of the following will receive on their savings accounts if the rate of interest is 6.5%.
   James €2000; Breda €5600; Maureen €780; Lil €1255.

2. Estimate the future cost of each of the following expenditures if the rate of increase is 5%.
   Mortgage €400; Car insurance €600; ESB €50; Car tax €90.

3. Complete a budget for the Murray household for the first four months of 1997, given the following information:

   Opening cash in hand was €100.

   Estimated income

   P. Murray earns €1000 net per month.
   M. Murray earns €1200 net per month.
   Child benefit is €40 per month.

   Estimated expenditure

   Annual car insurance €600 due in February.
   Annual car tax €100 due in January.
   Car loan repayments €300 per month.
   ESB bill is expected to be €100 in February and €80 in April.
   House mortgage is expected to be €300 per month.
   House insurance premium amounts to €100 per year payable in March.
   Entertainment costs expected to be €50 per month.
   Birthdays in February and March €80 each.
   Petrol costs per month €80.
   Household expenses per month €200.

4. Complete a budget for the Briody family for the first four months of 1997, given the following information:

   Opening cash in hand is €90.

   Expected income

   Paul Briody earns net €1200 per month.
   Kathleen Briody earns net €1300 per month.
   Child benefit €60 per month.

Expected expenditure

Household mortgage expected to be €350 per month.
Annual car tax expected to €150 due in January.
Groceries expected to be €250 per month.
Annual car insurance expected to be €450 due in March.
ESB bill in January expected to be €70 and in March expected to be €50.
Telephone bill in February expected to be €100 and in April expected to be €90.
Entertainment expected to be €60 per month.
Birthdays in February expected to cost €50.
Car running costs expected to be €100 per month except in February when the annual service to the car will cost an extra €45.

5. Complete a budget for the Kavanagh family for the months of June, July August and September, 1997 given the following details:

Opening cash in hand is €200.

Estimated income

T. Kavanagh earns €900 net per month, but she expects to get a bonus of €200 in August.
M. Kavanagh earns €800 net per month. He expects to get an increase of 2% starting in July.

Estimated expenditure

Groceries are usually €300 per month.
ESB bills are expected to be €60 in June and €50 in August.
House mortgage will be €400 per month.
Estimated annual car tax due in July €100
Telephone bill in June is expected to be €100 and in August €160.
Entertainment will cost €50 per month.
Birthdays in July are expected to cost €80.

6. Caroline earns €290 net per week. Her weekly expenses are:

Rent €70
Groceries $\frac{1}{3}$ of her earnings
ESB bill €12
Insurance policy €8
Entertainment €35
Bus fares €12
Remainder in savings.
(a) Calculate her grocery bill.
(b) (i) Draft her weekly budget. (ii) Calculate her savings.
(c) Caroline is due an increase in her net pay of 7% and is considering the purchase of a second-hand car. She reckons her petrol costs would be $1\frac{1}{2}$ times her present bus fare costs. What repayments could she afford to make per week if her other expenses did not increase and she reduced her level of savings by 50%?
(d) Draft her balancing budget.

7. Tom earns €350 per week net. His weekly expenses are:

Mortgage €90
Groceries $\frac{1}{4}$ of his earnings
ESB bill €10
Car running expenses €20
Entertainment €40
Remainder in savings.
(a) Calculate his grocery bill.
(b) (i) Draft his weekly budget. (ii) Calculate his savings.
(c) Tom is due an increase in his net pay of 3% and is considering the purchase of a dishwasher. What repayments could he afford to make per week if he reduced his level of savings by $33\frac{1}{3}\%$? He also plans to reduce his entertainment expenses by 20%. Assume all his other expenses do not change.
(d) Draft his balancing budget.

8. Helen earns €290 per week net. Her weekly expenses are:

Rent €75
Groceries $\frac{1}{4}$ of her earnings.
ESB bill €11
Entertainment €35
Bus fare €20
Remainder in savings.
(a) Calculate her groceries.
(b) (i) Draft her weekly budget. (ii) Calculate her savings.
(c) Helen is due an increase in her net pay of 8% and is considering the purchase of a second-hand car. She estimates that her petrol costs would be $1\frac{1}{2}$ times her present bus fare costs. Repairs and maintenance per week would be €20. What repayments could she afford to make per week if her other expenses did not increase and she reduced her savings by 25%?
(d) Draft her final budget.

CHAPTER 5
Basic statistics

In this chapter we will deal with:
— **calculation of the mean, the mode and the median**
— **tabulation of given data**
— **representing data diagrammatically**
— **interpreting statistical charts and graphs.**

THE MEAN (AVERAGE)

The mean is defined as $\dfrac{\text{Sum of item's values}}{\text{No. of items}}$.

Example 1

Calculate the mean output of ten workers given that their output in units is recorded as follows:

34, 35, 39, 29, 34, 38, 32, 35, 35, 30.

Answer

$\dfrac{34 + 35 + 39 + 29 + 34 + 38 + 32 + 35 + 35 + 30}{10}$

= 34.1 units.

THE MEDIAN

The median is defined as the value of the object which falls in the centre of the array or distribution.

Example 2

Find the median of the following output values:

43, 45, 46, 41, 49, 38, 47.

Answer

First arrange the numbers in ascending order:

38, 41, 43, 45, 46, 47, 49.

Then find the value which falls in the centre of the list. In this case the answer is 45 units.

Example 3

Find the median of the values in Example 1:

34, 35, 39, 29, 34, 38, 32, 35, 35, 30.

Answer

29 30 32 34 34 35 35 35 38 39

Since there is an even number of values we take the centre pair and divide their sum:

$$\frac{34 + 35}{2} = 34.5 \text{ units.}$$

THE MODE

The mode is defined as the value which occurs most frequently. It is possible that more than one mode can occur in a frequency distribution.

Example 4

Find the mode of the output values in Example 1:

34, 35, 39, 29, 34, 38, 32, 35, 35, 30.

Answer

First arrange the numbers in a table as shown:

	Worker output						
Value	29	30	32	34	35	38	39
Frequency	1	1	1	2	3	1	1

Then simply find the value which occurs most frequently. In this instance the value is 35 units.

Exercise 5.1

Find the mean, the mode and the median for questions 1-11.

1. 4, 5, 2, 1, 9, 7, 5, 6.

2. 21, 22, 16, 16, 10, 12, 13, 14, 19, 17.

3. 12, 9, 8, 16, 3, 5, 9, 10.

4. 47, 42, 43, 46, 43, 46, 45, 47, 46, 44, 45, 46.

5. 21, 14, 17, 11, 17, 17, 24, 14, 12, 20, 17, 20.

6. 24, 20, 26, 28, 28, 34, 32, 28, 26, 28, 32, 29, 28, 29.

7. 57, 62, 58, 59, 59, 58, 60, 59, 56, 61, 60.

8. 34, 29, 38, 31, 33, 33, 34, 36, 33, 31.

9. 71, 70, 63, 70, 76, 71, 65, 65, 71, 70, 72, 70.

10. 16, 14, 15, 14, 10, 15, 15, 13, 14, 14, 13, 11, 14, 11.

11. 36, 29, 28, 43, 37, 36, 34, 31, 38, 36, 35, 37, 32, 41.

12. A birdwatcher's club decided to take a survey of the nests of a particular species in an area of a forest. The purpose was to study the number of chicks in the nests. You have been asked to find the mean and the mode of the data the birdwatchers have collected. There were thirteen nests in the area and the numbers of chicks were as follows:

    2, 4, 1, 3, 1, 2, 2, 3, 1, 2, 3, 2, 1.

TABULATION OF DATA

In order to make data more readable and to simplify calculations, the data can be arranged in tables.

Frequency tables

Example 5

You conduct a survey of your class, 20 people, in order to find out the average number of children per family. Your results are:

    1, 3, 6, 1, 2, 2, 3, 3, 4, 3, 3, 4, 2, 5, 4, 2, 3, 4, 5, 4.

It is easy to see how difficult it is to perform any calculations on this, relatively short, list of data. To tabulate the data, first establish how many ones, twos, threes, etc. there are:

1 //
2 ////
3 //// /
4 ////
5 //
6 /

It is now easier to read the data; a glance will tell you that there is only one family with six children. The next step is to put the data into a table as follows:

No. of children	1	2	3	4	5	6
Frequency	2	4	6	5	2	1

The average number of children may now be calculated as follows:

Sum of all the children = (1).(2)+(2).(4)+(3).(6)+(4).(5)+(5).(2)+(6).(1)
$$= 2 + 8 + 18 + 20 + 10 + 6 = 64$$

Average number of children per family = $64/20 = 3.2$ children per family

Grouped frequency tables

Sometimes there are too many different values to tabulate as above; the resulting table may not be a significant improvement on the data provided. In these cases a grouped frequency table may prove more useful.

Example 6

You are working for a local manufacturing firm and have been asked to find the average output and the mode from a particular machine from data which has been collected hourly over the past week.

Output	9 am	10 am	11 am	12 pm	1 pm	3 pm	4 pm	5pm
Monday	34	25	39	38	47	40	29	32
Tuesday	40	36	35	43	24	37	48	31
Wednesday	36	41	27	41	47	34	38	42
Thursday	52	36	49	30	38	31	41	27
Friday	47	38	34	26	33	44	35	51

Answer

Although the data is in whole numbers and within a limited range a frequency table, as constructed in Example 5 above, would be only marginally more readable due to the variety of values. A more reasonable solution would be to divide the range into intervals and count the number of values which occur in each interval. In this case the following intervals would seem to be the most practical.

Output	21–25	26–30	31–35	36–40	41–45	46–50	51–55
Frequency	2	5	9	11	6	5	2

The mean may now be calculated as follows:

(a) Find the mid-interval value for each interval, e.g. $\dfrac{21 + 25}{2} = 23$
the mid-interval value = 23

(b) Use this value to calculate the mean as before.

$(23)(2) + (28)(5) + (33)(9) + (38)(11) + (43)(6) + (48)(5) + (53)(2)$
$= 46 + 140 + 297 + 418 + 258 + 240 + 106 = 1505$

Average output per hour $= \frac{1505}{40} = 37.625$ units.

The mode is simply the most frequently occurring interval. In this case that is 36–40.

Exercise 5.2

For questions 1 and 2 tabulate the data given.

1. 35, 36, 32, 34, 31, 35, 32, 35, 35, 36, 34, 33, 39, 38, 37, 37, 35, 34, 40.

2. 2, 1, 5, 6, 5, 13, 11, 6, 8, 7, 7, 2, 3, 6, 4, 10, 9, 4, 6, 8.

3. The number of people who visit an amusement park in one week in July is recorded below.

Patronage	9–10 am	10–11 am	11–12 am	12–1 pm	1–2 pm	2–3 pm	3–4 pm	4–5 pm
Monday	56	176	275	309	326	338	335	342
Tuesday	83	210	293	327	328	345	339	341
Wednesday	72	232	286	315	340	342	347	352
Thursday	69	196	316	306	337	351	349	347
Friday	58	241	323	328	341	352	359	351
Saturday	99	207	319	342	356	350	362	360

(a) Find the average number of patrons per hour from 11 am to 5 pm to the next whole number.
(b) If admission is €4 per person, what is the average takings per hour between 11 am and 5 pm?

For questions 4–10 tabulate the values given and find the mode and the mean.

4. 54, 52, 47, 49, 51, 53, 52, 57, 55, 52, 52, 53, 51, 53.

5. 61, 63, 71, 64, 65, 64, 69, 59, 66, 66, 68, 67, 66, 67, 60, 65, 68, 64.

6. 3, 6, 1, 8, 3, 2, 5, 4, 4, 6, 4, 1, 7, 4, 5, 7, 8, 2.

7. 53, 52, 58, 55, 55, 51, 61, 57, 58, 57, 52, 59, 54, 56, 57, 57, 58, 56.

8. 89, 84, 83, 90, 94, 88, 87, 84, 88, 91, 89, 92, 88, 87, 85, 88, 86, 89, 88, 90, 86, 88.

9. 15, 16, 12, 17, 14, 14, 13, 14, 15, 15, 14, 12, 16, 17, 16, 15, 14, 13, 16, 13, 14, 16, 12, 17, 15.

10. 34, 31, 26, 25, 30, 29, 30, 29, 32, 27, 28, 30, 29, 29, 28, 30, 29, 27, 33, 31, 31, 27, 29, 26, 29, 28, 31, 30.

For questions 11 and 12 tabulate the given data and find the mean.

11. 51, 89, 66, 40, 58, 79, 42, 61, 71, 54, 57, 48, 80, 45, 68, 71, 60, 82, 76, 63, 60, 77, 65, 74, 70.

12. The gross wages for five operatives in the factory in which you work are as follows:

Wages €	Week 1	Week 2	Week 3	Week 4
Operative 1	107	126	134	113
Operative 2	111	120	117	123
Operative 3	128	92	103	100
Operative 4	133	149	144	112
Operative 5	94	105	123	121

REPRESENTING DATA DIAGRAMMATICALLY

In order to make data more understandable, graphs and charts are used as visual aids. Therefore they need to be large and clear and to mean something to a person who is unfamiliar with the data.

Line (trend) graphs

A line graph shows the changes in a variable with respect to time.

Example 7

You are working for a hotel and have been asked to represent graphically the profits for the first half of the year for a presentation. The profits are tabulated below.

Month	Jan	Feb	March	April	May	June
Profit (€)	2150	2065	2230	2475	2585	2940

Answer

Plot the points with the independent variable in this case, month, on the x-axis, as shown below.

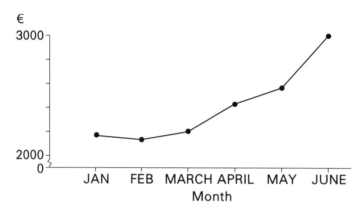

This graph clearly shows that for the first six months of the year there is an almost continuous rise in profits. Because there are no values below €2000, figures below this are indicated by a squiggle as in the diagram.

Bar charts

A bar chart is a diagram consisting of one or more bars in which the length of the bar indicates the magnitude of the data.

Example 8

Show the following profit data on a vertical bar chart.

Month	Jan	Feb	March	April	May
Profit (€)	3200	3600	3800	3400	3500

Answer

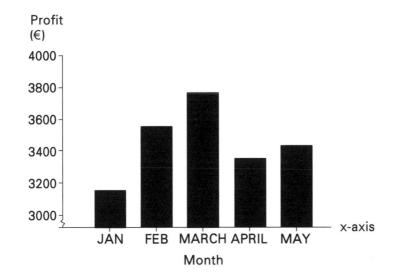

Again the independent variable is on the *x*-axis. This is known as a *vertical bar chart*. The axes may be swapped around to produce a *horizontal bar chart* as shown below. Note that for convenience the scale below €3000 has been omitted as there are no values below this. Always clearly indicate where your scale starts so as to avoid confusion.

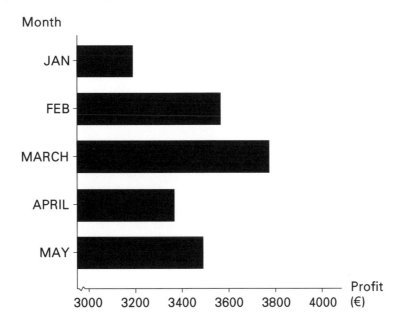

Component bar charts

Data may be composed of several different factors, i.e. the profits may have accrued from different sources, for example in a hotel the bar profits may be separate from the profits from the rooms.

Example 9

Graphically represent the following data:

Month	Jan	Feb	March	April	May
Profit – bar (€)	3200	3600	3800	3400	3500
Profit – hotel (€)	1500	1600	2000	2200	2300

Answer

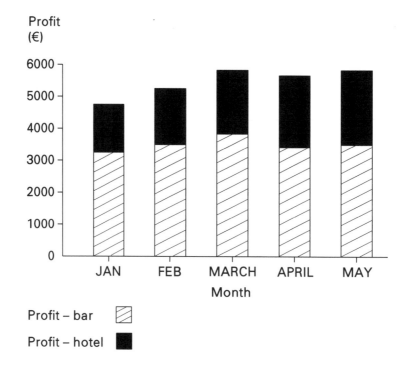

Compound bar charts

The above data may also be expressed in a compound bar chart. The difference between the two lies in what is the most important piece of information to be represented. While the component bar chart shows the total first and then how that is divided up, i.e. total sales is the most significant figure, the compound bar chart shows the breakdown first and the total may be obtained by addition.

Example 10

Represent the values from Example 9 using a compound bar chart.

Answer

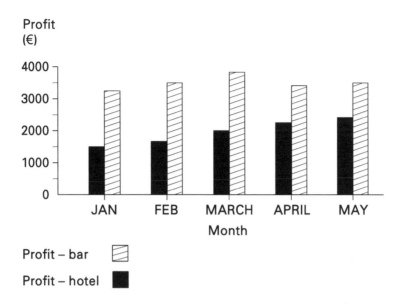

A compound bar chart is very useful for comparing two sets of figures.

Pictograms

A pictogram uses symbols to describe the relative sizes of given quantities. The symbols should be simple, clear and relevant to the data being measured. For money one could use bags, for example:

for every €500 use

for any amount less than €500 use

Example 11

Use a pictogram to describe the data given below:

Month	Jan	Feb	March	April	May
Profit (€)	3200	3600	4200	4500	5000

Answer

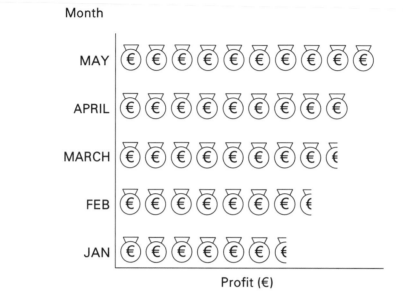

Each bag in this case represents €500. As can be seen from the above example, quantities smaller than the amount that the symbols stand for are not exactly represented, so while they are clear and easy to understand, pictograms are not as precise as either line graphs or bar charts.

Pie charts

In a pie chart the quantities are represented as sectors of a circle, the size of the sector corresponding to the size of the quantity.

Example 12

A farmer divides 60 hectares of his land between four different crops:

    Beet – 16 ha
    Hay – 20 ha
    Wheat – 18 ha
    Rapeseed – 6 ha

Show this information on a pie chart.

Answer

For each crop divide its area by the total area of land and multiply the answer by 360 to give the number of degrees.

Beet: $\dfrac{16}{60} \times 360 = 96°$ Wheat: $\dfrac{18}{60} \times 360 = 108°$

Hay: $\dfrac{20}{60} \times 360 = 120°$ Rapeseed: $\dfrac{6}{60} \times 360 = 36°$

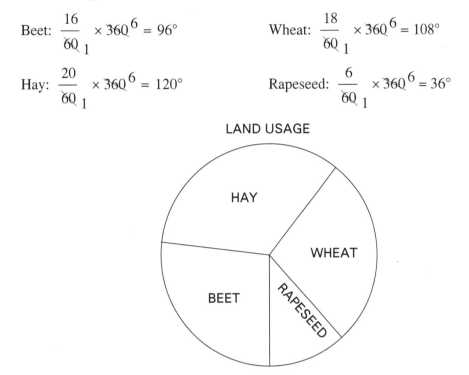

LAND USAGE

Example 13

720 people were asked where their savings were invested. Their answers are shown below on a pie chart.

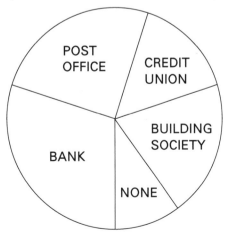

Find how many people are represented by each sector.

Answer

Using a protractor we find the size of each angle to be as follows:

> Bank: represented by an angle of 108°
> Post Office: represented by an angle of 90°
> Credit Union: represented by an angle of 54°
> Building Society: represented by an angle of 72°
> None: represented by an angle of 36°

> Bank: $(\frac{108}{360})$ $(720) = 216$ people
> Post Office: $(\frac{90}{360})(720) = 180$ people
> Credit Union: $(\frac{54}{360})(720) = 108$ people
> Building Society $(\frac{72}{360})(720) = 144$ people
> None: $(\frac{36}{360})(720) = 72$ people

Histograms

Histograms look like bar charts but there is an important difference. On a histogram the area of the bar is important, not the height, as this is where the information is recorded.

Example 14

Represent the following data in the form of a histogram.

Result	1	2	3	4	5
Frequency	2	4	7	6	1

Answer

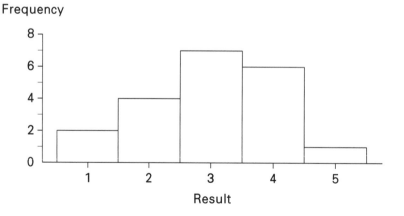

Here all the bar widths are the same so the height is proportional to the frequency.

Example 15

Represent the following data on a histogram:

Wages (€)	71–80	81–100	101–110	Worker's wages 111–115	116–130	131–150	151–170
No. of workers	5	12	17	10	21	10	2

Answer

(a) The width of each interval given above is different in this case so a *standard width* (interval), i.e. the most frequently occurring interval size, must be chosen, in this case, twenty.

(b) To determine the height of each bar, each frequency is divided by the actual interval and multiplied by the standard interval.

For example, for the interval (€71–80) the height is given by: $5(20/10) = 10$

Interval (€)	Width	Frequency	Adjustment	Height
71–80	10	5	20/10	10
81–100	20	12	20/20	12
101–110	10	17	20/10	34
111–115	5	10	20/5	40
116–130	15	21	20/15	28
131–150	20	10	20/20	10
151–170	20	2	20/20	2

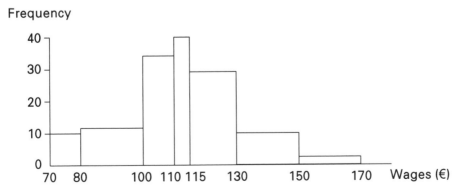

Worker's wages histogram

Example 16

The grades awarded to a class of 30 are represented on the histogram below. Find how many people fall into each interval.

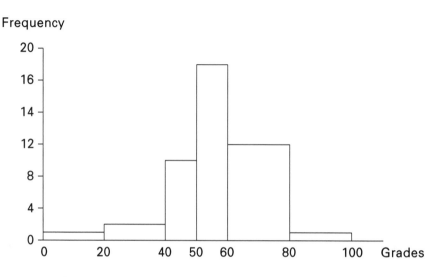

Answer

(a) Find the area of each 'bar'.

(b) Find the total area.

(c) Divide the total area by the number of students to get the standard interval width.

(d) Divide each area by the standard width to find the number of students in each interval.

(a) $0–20 : (20)(1) = 20$
    $20–40 : (20)(2) = 40$
    $40–50 : (10)(10) = 100$
    $50–60 : (10)(18) = 180$
    $60–80 : (20)(12) = 240$
    $80–100 : (20)(1) = 20$

(b) $20 + 40 + 50 + 180 + 240 + 20 = 600$

(c) $600/30 = 20$

(d) $0\text{-}20 : 20/20 = 1$ student
    $20\text{-}40 : 40/20 = 2$ students
    $40\text{-}50 : 100/20 = 5$ students
    $50\text{-}60 : 180/20 = 9$ students
    $60\text{-}80 : 240/20 = 12$ students
    $80\text{-}100 : 20/20 = 1$ student

Exercise 5.3

For questions 1–3 represent each of the tables using:

(a) a line graph
(b) a bar chart
(c) a pictogram.

1. Sales figures

Day	Mon	Tues	Wed	Thurs	Fri
Sales (€)	500	490	470	560	590

2. Test grades

Result	1	2	3	4	5
Frequency	12	28	52	36	8

3. Hospital admissions

Day	Mon	Tues	Wed	Thurs	Fri	Sat	Sun
No. of admissions	40	42	45	40	50	45	20

For questions 4 and 5 represent each of the sets of data using:

(a) a compound bar chart
(b) a component bar chart
(c) line graphs on the same axes
(d) a pie chart for each entry.

4. Profits

Month	Jan	Feb	March	April	May
Profit – bar (€)	6200	6700	6900	5900	6900
Profit – hotel (€)	1800	2200	2400	2500	2700

5. Employee numbers

Year	1991	1992	1993	1994	1995
Male employees	32	36	38	34	38
Female employees	15	17	24	28	28

6. Represent the following sets of data on pie charts.
  (a) Total income = €200 pw
      Rent = €40 pw
      Food = €50 pw
      Entertainment = €30 pw
      Transport = €10 pw
      Miscellaneous = €20 pw
      Savings = €50 pw
  (b) A student keeps her savings in a variety of accounts, two in a bank, one in a credit
      union and one in a post office.
      Total savings: €1800
      Bank Account 1: €900
      Bank Account 2: €500
      Credit Union: €200
      Post Office: €200
  (c) A farmer cultivates a number of crops. The percentage of land under each crop is
      recorded below.
      Wheat: 50%
      Barley: 20%
      Oats: 10%
      Other: 20%

7. Represent each of the following tables on a histogram.
  (a)

Result	1	2	3	4	5
Frequency	6	9	14	11	8

  (b)

Result	10	20	30	40	50	60
Frequency	2	7	14	15	9	2

  (c)

Result	5	6	7	8	9	10	11
Frequency	3	10	20	29	16	4	1

  (d)

Result	2	4	6	8	10
Frequency	1	7	10	5	3

8. Represent the following data on histograms.
   (a) (Note: In this instance 10–20 means excluding 10 but including 20.)

Interval	0–10	10–20	20–30	30–40	40–50	50–60	60–70
Frequency	5	12	15	25	18	10	2

(b)

Interval	1–5	6–10	11–15	16–20	21–25	26–30	31–35
Frequency	2	9	15	18	13	5	0

(c)

Interval	0–20	20–40	40–50	50–60	60–80	80–100
Frequency	5	12	15	25	18	10

(d)

Wages (€)	81–100	101–110	111–120	121–125	126–135	135–155
No. of employees	1	7	15	12	16	6

9. A total of 1080 people were surveyed to establish the political party they support. The information is shown on the pie chart below. Determine the percentage support enjoyed by each of the four main parties and the number of people who answered 'none'.

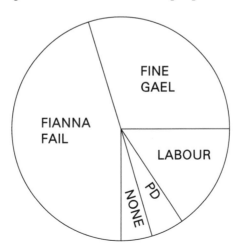

10. Find how much Sarah spends on food and rent given the pie chart below, if her total income is €300.

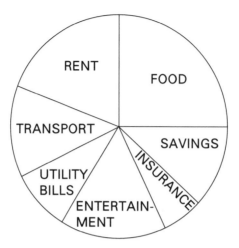

11. Find the frequency of each interval, if the standard width is 10.

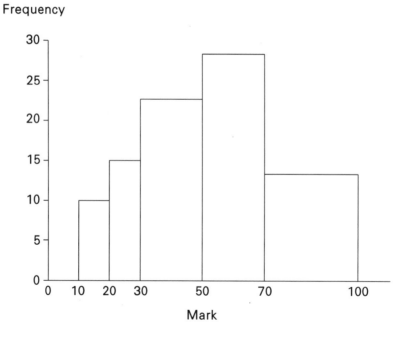

12. The grades awarded to a class of 23 students are shown below on a histogram. Find the number of students in each interval.

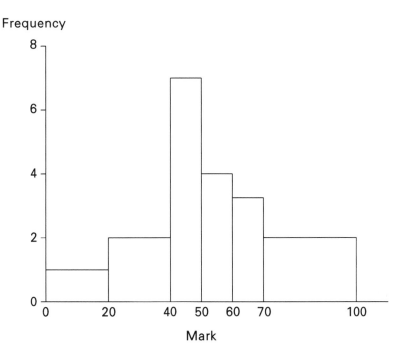

CHAPTER 6
Wages and taxation

In this chapter we will deal with:
— **gross wages**
— **Tax Credit System**
— **PAYE and PRSI**
— **tax deduction cards.**

WAGES

Wages are classed as earned income. A waged person is paid by the hour, so the income may fluctuate from week to week as the person works more or less hours.

Example 1

Five employees in your firm earn €5.22 per hour. Calculate their week's wages on the basis of the number of hours worked as shown below. Overtime is paid at time and a half over 39 hours.

Employee no.	No. of hours
A00212	39.2
A00192	38
A00203	35.48
A00204	39.92
A00197	43.01

(Note: This system is decimalised; the wages are calculated down to $\frac{1}{100}$ of an hour).

Answer

Overtime rate = $5.22 + (\frac{5.22}{2}) = 5.22 + 2.61 = €7.83$

A00212

Ordinary wages for 39 hours: $(39)(5.22) = €203.58$
Overtime for 0.2 hours: $(0.2)(7.83) = €1.57$
Total = €205.15

A00192

Ordinary wages for 38 hours: $(38)(5.22) = €198.36$
Total = €198.36

A00203

Ordinary wages for 35.48 hours: $(35.48)(5.22) = €185.21$
Total = €185.21

A00204

Ordinary wages for 39 hours: $(39)(5.22) = €203.58$
Overtime for 0.92 hours: $(0.92)(7.83) = €7.21$
Total = €210.79

A00197

Ordinary wages for 39 hours: $(39)(5.22) = €203.58$
Overtime for 4.01 hours: $(4.01)(7.83) = €31.40$
Total = €234.98

Example 2

Calculate the wages of the following employees. As before, overtime is over 39 hours and is paid at time and a half.

Employee no.	No. of hours	Rate of pay (€ per hour)
B00012	37 hrs 45 mins	5.22
B00013	39 hrs 20 mins	4.96
B00027	40 hrs 40 mins	5.22
B00053	39 hrs 12 mins	5.50

Answer

B00012

Overtime rate: €7.83
Ordinary wages for 37 hrs 45 mins: $(37.75)(5.22) = €197.06$
Total = €197.06

B00013

Overtime rate: €7.44
Ordinary wages for 39 hrs: $(39)(4.96) = €193.44$
Overtime for 20 mins: $(\frac{1}{3})(7.83) = €2.61$
Total = €196.05

B00027
    Overtime rate: €7.83
    Ordinary wages for 39 hrs: $(39)(5.22) = €203.58$
    Overtime for 1 hrs 40 mins: $(1\frac{1}{3})(7.83) = €13.05$
    Total $= €216.63$

B00053
    Overtime rate: €8.25
    Ordinary wages for 39 hrs: $(39)(5.50) = €214.50$
    Overtime for 12 mins: $(0.2)(8.25) = €1.65$
    Total $= €216.15$

Exercise 6.1

1. Calculate the wages for the following workers. The basic rate of pay is €4.72 per hour, with an overtime rate of €7.08 per hour over 39 hours.

Employee	No. of hours
A	28
B	37
C	39
D	43
E	35
F	46

2. The details of seven employees are listed below. Calculate their gross wages. Overtime is paid over 39 hours.

Employee	Rate of pay (€)	Overtime rate (€)	No. of hours
11	4.80	7.20	29
12	5.30	7.95	43
13	5.10	7.65	30
14	5.10	7.65	32.5
15	4.80	7.20	41
16	4.80	7.20	33
17	4.80	7.20	30

3. Calculate the gross wages of the following people. Overtime is paid over 40 hours.

Employee	Rate of pay (€)	Overtime rate (€)	No. of hours
21	6.00	9.00	42 hrs 30 mins
22	5.20	7.80	42 hrs 15 mins
23	4.96	7.44	42 hrs 30 mins
24	6.00	9.00	42 hrs 30 mins
25	4.96	7.44	42 hrs 15 mins
26	5.20	7.80	40 hrs
27	6.00	9.00	42 hrs 30 mins

4. Calculate the gross wages of these employees given the following details. Overtime is paid over 40 hours.

Employee	Rate of pay (€)	Overtime rate (€)	No. of hours
C00102	5.40	8.10	39
C00103	5.96	8.94	41
C00104	5.40	8.10	43
C00105	5.40	8.10	46
C00106	5.56	8.34	48
C00107	6.00	9.00	41
C00108	5.96	8.94	41

INCOME TAX

Tax is collected by the PAYE (Pay As You Earn) method. The tax is deducted at source by the employer and it is paid weekly, fortnightly or monthly, depending on when the employee is paid.

It is a tax credit PAYE system. Each employee is given tax credits and a standard rate cut-off point. These are used in the calculation of tax for each pay period (e.g. weekly, monthly).

What are tax credits?

Under a tax credit system you are entitled to tax credits depending on your personal circumstances, e.g. married person's tax credit, employee (PAYE) tax credit etc.

These tax credits are used to reduce tax calculated on your gross pay. Tax credits are non-refundable. However, any unused tax credits in a pay week or month are carried forward to subsequent pay period(s) within the tax year.

Definition of a standard rate cut-off point

A Standard Rate Cut-Off Point is the amount of your personal standard rate tax band as adjusted – downwards for any non-PAYE income and upwards for any tax reliefs available at the higher rate of tax.

For each pay period, you pay tax at the standard rate of tax up to the cut-off point. Any income over the cut-off point is taxed at the higher rate of tax.

Non PAYE Income

Where an employee has non-PAYE income, e.g. benefit-in-kind (the tax on which is collected through the PAYE system), the tax credits are *reduced* by the amount of the non-PAYE income at the standard rate of tax and the standard rate tax band is *reduced* by the amount of that income.

Reducing the tax credits ensures the non-PAYE income is taxed at the standard rate of tax. Reducing the standard rate tax band ensures the income is taxed at the difference between the standard rate and the higher rate of tax.

The combined effect is to collect tax due on the non-PAYE income at the higher rate of tax.

Reliefs Due at the Higher Rate of Tax

Where an employee has deductions from income e.g. expenses of employment, which qualify for tax relief at the higher rate of tax, the tax credits are *increased* by the amount of the relief at the standard rate of tax and the standard rate tax band is also *increased* by the amount of the relief.

Increasing the tax credits ensures relief is obtained at the standard rate of tax. Increasing the standard rate tax band ensures relief is obtained at the difference between the standard rate and the higher rate of tax.

The combined effect ensures relief is obtained in full at the higher rate of tax.

Tax Rates and Tax Bands

There are different standard rate tax bands depending on the personal circumstances of the employee. Have a look at the chart on page 97.

Chart 1

Personal Circumstances	Bands of Taxable Income
Single/Widowed without dependent children	€25 400 @ 20% Balance @ 42%
Single/Widowed qualifying for One-Parent Family	€29 400.50 @ 20% Balance @ 42%
Married couple (one spouse with income)	€36 830 @ 20% Balance @ 42%
Married couple (both spouses with income)	€36 830 @ 20% [with increase of €13 970 max.] Balance @ 42%

In this example tax rates are 20% and 42%

Note 1

(a) Tax credit for rent relief is available to an employee depending on personal circumstances.

Have a look at the following chart.

Chart 2

Personal Circumstances	Tax credits
Single	
Under 55 Max.	€254
Over 55 Max.	€508
Widowed	
Under 55 Max.	€508
Over 55 Max.	€1016
Married	
Under 55 Max.	€508
Over 55 Max.	€1016

(b) Medical Insurance premiums tax relief is granted 'at source'. This means that the tax relief element will be netted off against gross premium. At a standard rate of income tax, subscribers will pay a reduced premium to the medical insurer.

(c) Where the employer deducts Permanent Health Benefit scheme contributions from the employee's gross pay, the tax relief will be given at source.

(d) There is a tax credit for trade union subscription.

(e) Where an employee lets a room as residential accommodation in his/her principal private residence, a proportion of the gross annual rental income will be exempt from tax. This may vary from year to year.

(f) Employees on low incomes are exempt from tax. The following chart sets out the limits.

Chart 3

Personal Circumstances	
Single/Widowed	
General Limit (under 65 years of age)	€5 207
65 years of age and over	€10 795
Married	
General Limit (under 65 years of age)	€10 417
65 years of age and over	€21 590

Calculation of weekly/monthly tax

An employee's weekly/monthly gross pay is taxed as follows:

- The standard rate of tax is applied to gross pay up to the *standard rate cut-off point* for that pay week or month.

- Any balance of pay over that amount in that pay period is taxed at the higher rate of tax.

- The sum of these two figures gives the gross weekly/monthly tax.

- This gross tax is reduced by the *tax credits* to arrive at the net tax payable, i.e.
  GROSS TAX LESS TAX CREDITS = TAX PAYABLE.

Example 3

Mary, a single person, earns €600 per week.
Her tax credits are €50 per week.
Her standard rate cut-off point is €400 per week.
Tax is at 20% standard rate and 42% higher rate.
Calculate her tax payable:

$$\text{Gross tax: } 400 \times 20\% = 80$$
$$200 \times 42\% = 84$$
$$\overline{164}$$

Tax Payable = Gross Tax less Tax Credits
$$164 - 50 = 114$$

Tax payable is €114.

Example 4

M. O'Grady is single. She owns her own home and has a monthly income of €2 620. She has a monthly standard rate cut-off point of €1 674 and monthly tax credits of €154.
Calculate her tax payable.

€1 674 × 20% = €334.80
€2 620 − €1 674 = €946 × 42% = €397.32
Gross Tax = €334.80 + €397.32 = €732.12
Tax Payable = €732.12 − €154 = €578.12

Example 5

A married couple (one spouse earning) have a gross income of €921.05 per week. They have a standard rate cut-off point of €564.74 per week and tax credits of €58.43 per week.
Calculate their pay after tax.

Tax on €564.74 @ 20% = €112.94
Tax on €356.31 @ 42% = €149.65
Gross Tax = €262.59
Less Tax Credits = €58.43
Tax payable this week = €204.16
Pay after tax = €921.74 − €204.16 = €717.48

Exercise 6.2

Note: In this exercise tax is at 20% standard rate and 42% higher rate.

1. Mary and Patrick are married. Mary is a housewife. Patrick has a salary of €30 300. Their relevant tax details are as follows:

   Standard rate cut-off point: €25 848 per annum
   Tax credits: €2 448 per annum.

   Calculate their annual tax bill.

2. Paul is single and has a gross annual income of €27 040.
   He has a standard rate cut-off point of €18 888 and tax credits of €1 608.
   Calculate Paul's weekly income after tax.

3. Sylvia is a widow. She has a gross income of €21 840.
   She has a standard rate cut-off point of €15 480 and tax credits of €1 350.
   Calculate her annual tax bill.

4. Brian and Ann are both working. They have a combined annual income of €56 840.
   They have a standard rate cut-off point of €30 720 and tax credits of €3 180.
   Brian is allocated €21 900 of the standard rate cut-off point and €2 800 of the tax credits.
   If his income is €42 680, calculate his monthly tax bill.

5. John is a single PAYE employee with a gross monthly salary of €2 500. The tax office has calculated his monthly standard rate cut-off point to be €1 644.45 and his tax credits to be €123.34. Calculate his monthly tax bill.

6.   Jane has a gross monthly salary of £2 500. She is married and this is taken into account by the tax office when calculating her monthly standard rate cut-off point. Her monthly standard rate cut-off point is €238.45 and her tax credits are €213.75 per month. Calculate her monthly tax bill.

PRSI

PRSI stands for pay related social insurance. A portion of this comes out of your wages and the rest is paid by your employer. There are different rates depending on which class you belong to. Your class is determined by your wages, your occupation and whether you receive any benefits from the Department of Social, Community and Family Affairs.

Note 2

Each person is allocated a PPS number (Personal Public Service number). This number, which replaces the previous PRSI number, must be quoted when contacting the tax office or Department of Social, Community and Family Affairs.

Example 6

Margaux Mulally is single and earns €300 per week. Her tax credits are €25. Her standard rate cut-off point is €250. Tax rates are 20% up to standard rate cut-off point and 42% on the rest. She pays PRSI at 4.5%.

Answer

PAYE
Gross Wages per week €300
Tax: (a) cut-off point × 20%
€250 × 0.20 = €50
(b) Rest of income × 42%
€50 × 0.42 = €21
Gross Tax per week is (a) plus (b)
= €50 + €21
= €71
Tax payable per week = Gross Tax less Tax Credits
= €71 − €25
= €46

PRSI
4.5% of €300 = €13.50

Take Home Pay	€
= Gross Wages	300.00
less PAYE	46.00
	254.00
less PRSI	13.50
	240.50

Example 7

Diarmuid McMurrogh is single and earns €20 400 p.a. His tax credits are €100 per month. His monthly standard rate cut-off point is €1 000. Tax rates are 20% up to standard rate cut-off point and 42% on the rest. Calculate his take-home pay if he pays PRSI monthly at 4.5%.

Answer

PAYE
Gross Earnings per month 20 400/12 = €1 700
Gross Tax:
(a) Standard rate cut-off point × 20%
= €1 000 × 20%
= €200
(b) Rest of income × 42%
= €700 × 42%
= €294
Gross Tax = (a) plus (b)
= €200 + €294
= €494
Tax Payable = Gross Tax − Tax Credits
= €494 − €100
= €394

PRSI
€1,700 × 4.5%
= €76.50

Take Home Pay:	€
Gross Earnings per month	1 700.00
less PAYE	394.00
	1 306.00
less PRSI	76.50
Take Home Pay	€1 229.50

Example 8

Owen and Mairéad O'Brien are married. Mairéad is a housewife and has no income of her own. Owen earns €30 000 p.a. His standard rate cut-off point per month is €2 000. His tax credits per month are €210. Tax rates are 20% up to standard rate cut-off point and 42% on the rest of the income. Calculate his take-home pay if he pays PRSI monthly at 4.5%.

Answer

PAYE
Gross wages per month = 30 000/12 = €2 500
Gross Tax per month is (a) cut-off point × 20%
= €2 000 × 20% = €400
(b) Rest of income × 0.42
€500 × 0.42 = €210

Gross Tax per month = (a) + (b)
= €400 + €210
= €610
Tax Payable = Gross Tax − Tax Credits
= €610 − €210
= €400

PRSI
€2 500 × 4.5%
= €112.50

Take Home Pay:	€
Gross Earnings per month	2 500
less PAYE	400
	2 100
less PRSI	112.50
Take Home Pay	€1 987.50

Exercise 6.3

Note: In this exercise tax is at 20% standard rate and 42% higher rate.

1. John is paid €8.20 per hour for a 39 hour week. He is paid time and a half for each hour over 39 hours. He has a standard rate cut-off point of €280 per week and he has tax credits of €32 per week. If John works a 44 hour week and pays PRSI at 4.5% calculate
   (a) his gross earnings
   (b) his total tax bill
   (c) the amount of PRSI he pays
   (d) his net income.

2. Mary earns a basic wage of €312 for a 39 hour week. For up to 2 hours overtime she is paid time and a half; after that she is paid double time. She has a weekly standard rate cut-off point of €252 per week and tax credits of €28 per week. If she works 45 hours per week and pays PRSI at 2.15%, calculate
   (a) her gross earnings
   (b) her total tax bill
   (c) the amount of PRSI paid
   (d) her net income.

3. Steve earns €8.50 per hour. He works a 39 hour week. He also receives a bonus of 20% on his basic wages. He has a standard rate cut-off point of €380 per week and tax credits of €38 per week. If he pays PRSI at 3.9% after the first €120, calculate
   (a) his gross earnings
   (b) his total tax bill
   (c) the amount of PRSI paid
   (d) his net income.

4. Copy and complete this section of Stephen Roche's tax deduction card. His gross earnings per month are recorded as also are his standard rate cut-off point and his tax credits.

Employee's Name Mr Stephen Roche				PRSI No. 3456789A	Total Tax Credit €1 110		Total Cut-off Point €14 800			
Month No.	Gross Pay	Cumulative Gross Pay	Cumulative Standard Rate Cut-off Point	Cumulative Tax Due at Standard Rate	Cumulative Tax Due at Higher Rate	Cumulative Gross Tax	Cumulative Tax Credits	Cumulative Tax	Tax Deducted This Period
1	€2 400.00	€2 400.00	1 644.45	328.89	317.33	646.22	123.34	522.88	522.88
2	€1 600.00	€4 000.00	3 288.89	657.77	298.66	956.44	246.68	709.87	186.88
3	€2 000.00								
4	€2 500.00								
5	€3 500.00								
6	€2 000.00								
7	€2 000.00								
8	€2 000.00								
9	€2 000.00								

CHAPTER 7

Calculations of costing in relation to the retail trade

In this chapter we will deal with:
— VAT – inclusive and exclusive
— calculations on gross/net profit and selling prices
— discounts
— foreign currency
— the euro.

VAT (value added tax) – inclusive and exclusive

VAT (value added tax) is imposed by the government on the invoice price charged for any goods or services supplied. An invoice might look like this:

Goods total price	€10 000
Plus VAT @ $12\frac{1}{2}$%	€ 1 250
	————
Total invoice	€11 250

The supplier collects the €1250 which is called output tax because it has been added to one of his/her sales (outputs). The net proceeds of VAT (output tax – input tax) must be paid over at regular intervals to the collector general of the revenue commissioners.
The three rates of VAT in Ireland are:

0%
$12\frac{1}{2}$%
20%

Example 1

A computer manufacture has received an order for 50 computers at €896 each. VAT is charged at $12\frac{1}{2}$%. What is the total cost of this order?

Answer

50 computers at €896 each = €896 × 50 = €44 800

VAT = $12\frac{1}{2}\%$

therefore €44 800 × 0.125 = €5600

Total cost of order

Sales   €44 800

+ VAT   € 5 600
_____

€50 400

Exercise 7.1

1. Work out the VAT payable on the following sales if VAT is levied at $12\frac{1}{2}\%$.

   (a) €280
   (b) €9800
   (c) €20 800
   (d) €9842.90
   (e) €624
   (f) €24 961.24

Example 2

If the total invoice cost was €800 and VAT is levied at 21%, what was the price before VAT was added?

Answer

€800 represents 100% + 21%, i.e. 121% of the price before VAT was added on:

$$121\% = €800$$

$$1\% = \frac{€800}{121}$$

$$100\% = \frac{€800}{121} \times \frac{100}{1}$$

$$= €661.16$$

The price before VAT was added was €661.16.

Exercise 7.2

1. What is the VAT at 20% on each of the total invoice figures shown below?

   (a) €5860.12
   (b) €281
   (c) €942.60
   (d) €967.99
   (e) €2199.63
   (f) €289.99

2. An electrical shop sells a television set for a price which includes VAT at $12\frac{1}{2}\%$. If the VAT content of the price is €62.50, at which price does the shop sell the television set?

3. A computer company at the end of one particular day has sold goods to the total value of €21 900. If this amount included VAT at 21%, calculate the price of the goods before VAT was added on.

4. Mike Green sold his house for €60 000. Out of this he paid an auctioneer 3% of the sale price and a solicitor €425. Mike then paid VAT at the rate of 21% on both the solicitor's and auctioneer's fees. Calculate the total amount of VAT he paid.

GROSS AND NET PROFIT

Gross profit

Gross profit is defined as the selling price minus the cost price.

Example 3

A retailer buys an item for €4.00. He then sells it on to a customer at a price of €6.00. What is his gross profit?

Answer

Selling price	€6.00
– Cost price	€4.00
Gross profit	€2.00

Example 4

A retailer buys an item for €9.50. He makes a profit of 20%. What is his selling price and what is gross profit?

Answer

Cost price = €9.50
20% of €9.50 = €1.90 = Gross profit
Selling price = €9.50 + €1.90 = €11.40

Example 5

A retailer buys a batch of 20 items at €65 a piece. He sells 14 of these items at €90 and 6 items at €80. What is his total profit?

Answer

Selling price	€90
− Cost price	€65
= Gross profit	€25

Selling price	€80
− Cost price	€65
= Gross profit	€15

Gross profit on 14 items: $(25)(14) = €350$
Gross profit on 6 items: $(15)(6) = €90$
Total $= €350 + €90 = €440$

Net profit

Net profit is defined as the total gross profit minus the cost of sales (including overheads, wages, salaries, etc.). It is calculated at the end of the year.

Example 6

Find the net profit if:

Gross profit $= €15\ 000$
Cost of sales $= €10\ 000$

Answer

Gross profit	€15 000
− Cost of sales	€10 000
Net profit	€ 5 000

Example 7

Find the net profit if:

Gross profit $= €120\ 000$
Wages $= €30\ 000$
Salaries $= €20\ 000$
Electricity $= €4000$
Expenses $= €1000$

Answer

Wages	€ 30 000
Salaries	€ 20 000
Electricity	€ 4 000
+ Expenses	€ 1 000
Cost of sales	€ 55 000
Gross profit	€120 000
– Cost of sales	€ 55 000
Net profit	€ 65 000

Exercise 7.3

1. Find the gross profit in each of the following cases.
   (a) Selling price = €4.99, Cost price = €3.00
   (b) Selling price = €13, Cost price = €10
   (c) Selling price = €10, Cost price = €7.50
   (d) Selling price = €299.99, Cost price = €230
   (e) Selling price = €1500, Cost price = €1000
   (f) Selling price = €499, Cost price = €350
   (g) Selling price = €6.99, Cost price = €4.00
   (h) Selling price = €14.50, Cost price = €10

2. Find the gross profit and selling price in each of the following cases.
   (a) Cost price = €6.00, Gross profit = 50%
   (b) Cost price = €24, Gross profit = 25%
   (c) Cost price = €6.50, Gross profit = 30%
   (d) Cost price = €70, Gross profit = 20%
   (e) Cost price = €200, Gross profit = 35%
   (f) Cost price = €5, Gross profit = 45%
   (g) Cost price = €150, Gross profit = 60%

3. What is the gross profit in each of the following cases.
   (a) A television sales firm buys 25 televisions at €150 each. It then sells 15 televisions for €200 and 10 televisions for €220.
   (b) A retailer buys 50 items at €1 a piece and sells 20 of them at €1.50 and the remainder at €1.75.
   (c) A retailer buys 100 items at €12 each. 30 are sold at €18 each, 30 are sold at €15 each and the remainder are sold at €19 each.

4. Find the net price in each of the following cases.
   (a) Gross profit = €50 000, Cost of sales = €35 000
   (b) Gross profit = €90 000, Cost of sales = €57 000
   (c) Gross profit = €102 000, Cost of sales = €76 000
   (d) Gross profit = €25 000, Cost of sales = €22 000

5. Calculate the net profit in each case
   (a) Gross profit = €24 000
       Wages = €10 000
       Electricity = €2000
       Gas = €950
       Advertising = €1300
       Expenses = €1780
   (b) Gross profit = €35 000
       Wages = €12 000
       Utility bills = €3000
       Advertising = €2500
       Expenses = €1260
   (c) Gross profit = €183 000
       Wages = €45 900
       Electricity = €2700
       Gas = €780
       Telephone = €500
       Advertising = €10 300
       Expenses = €3560
   (d) Gross profit = €205 000
       Wages = €54 000
       Utility bills = €3860
       Advertising = €32 500
       Telephone = €788
       Equipment leasing = €15 000
       Expenses = €7780

DISCOUNTS

Cash discount: given by the retailer to the customer as an incentive to pay cash immediately.
Trade discount: given by the wholesaler/manufacturer to the retailer. Sometimes this discount is the retailer's gross profit, i.e. the retailer sells the goods at cost price and the trade discount yields the profit.
Quantity/bulk discount: this is an extra discount the seller gives the buyer if large quantities of goods are bought. It is an incentive to buy in bulk.
Seasonal discount: this is a discount for buying out of season.
Anticipation discount: this is a discount for early payment of debts, before they are due to be paid.

Example 8

A trader buys the following items:

10 dishwashers @ €140 each
12 refrigerators @ €190 each
15 kettles @ €12 each
15 toasters @ €12 each.

He receives a trade discount of 25%. Calculate how much he pays. If he gives a cash discount of 10% on his refrigerators (selling price €190 each), how much will a refrigerator cost a customer and what will the trader's profit on each refrigerator be?

Answer

10 dishwashers @ €140 each	€1400
12 refrigerators @ €190 each	€2280
15 kettles @ €12 each	€ 180
15 toasters @ €12 each	€ 180
Total cost	€4040
− Trade discount	€1010
Cash paid	€3030

Refrigerator
Selling price = €190
− Cash discount = €190 × 0.10 = €19
Price = €190 − €19 = €171 = Cost to customer
Profit = (25% − 10%) of €190 = 15% of €190 = €28.50 = Trader's profit

Example 9

A retailer buys some products @ €12 each. He receives a trade discount of 20%. If he also receives a bulk discount of 10% when he purchases in excess of 100 items at one time, calculate how much he pays when he buys 110 items.

Answer

110 @ €12 each = €1320
20% of €1320 = €264
10% of €1320 = €132
Cash paid = €1320 − (€264 − €132) = €1320 − €396 = €924

Example 10

A retailer buys Christmas decorations in June. She receives a trade discount of 20%, a bulk discount of 10% when buying more than 200 items, and a seasonal discount of 5%. Calculate the cost price if she buys 250 items at €1 each.

Answer

250 items @ €1 = €250
20% of €250 = €50
10% of €250 = €25
5% of €250 = €12.50
Cash paid = €250 − (€50 + €25 + €12.50) = €250 − €87.50 = €162.50

Example 11

A retailer buys Christmas decorations in July @ €5 a lot. He receives a trade discount of 15%, a bulk discount of 10% when he buys more than 200 lots, a seasonal discount of 5% and an anticipation discount of 5% if the payment is more than ten days early. Calculate the cash paid if:

(a) he buys 150 lots and pays 5 days early

(b) he buys 150 lots and pays 15 days early

(c) he buys 250 lots and pays 15 days early.

Answer

(a) 150 lots @ €5 each = €750
15% of €750 = €112.50 (trade discount)
5% of €750 = €37.50 (seasonal discount)
Cash paid = €750 − (€112.50 + €37.50) = €750 − €150 = €600

(b) 150 lots @ €5 each = €750
15% of €750 = €112.50 (trade discount)
5% of €750 = €37.50 (seasonal discount)
5% of €750 = €37.50 (anticipation discount)
Cash paid = €750 − (€112.50 + €37.50 + €37.50) = €750 − €187.50
= €562.50

(c) 250 lots @ €5 each = €1250
15% of €1250 = €187.50 (trade discount)
10% of €1250 = €125 (bulk discount)
5% of €1250 = €62.50 (seasonal discount)
5% of €1250 = €62.50 (anticipation discount)
Cash paid = €1250 − (€187.50 + €125 + €62.50 = €62.50)
= €1250 − €437.50
= €812.50

Exercise 7.4

1. Find the price the customer pays in each case.
    (a) Selling price €8.00, Cash discount 10%
    (b) Selling price €18.50, Cash discount 10%
    (c) Selling price €3.00, Cash discount 15%
    (d) Selling price €30.00, Cash discount 10%
    (e) Selling price €152.00, Cash discount 15%

2. Find the profit the retailer makes in each case. (Assume in each case that the selling price before the discount is the same as the cost price.)
    (a) Cost price €10.00, Trade discount 25%, Cash discount 10%
    (b) Cost price €4.20, Trade discount 25%, Cash discount 10%
    (c) Cost price €190.00, Trade discount 25%, Cash discount 15%

3. How much does the retailer pay for the goods for each of the following. (Assume that in each case the bulk discount is allowed.)
   (a) 200 items @ €3.50 each, Trade discount 20%, Bulk discount 10%
   (b) 150 items @ €8.00 each, Trade discount 25%, Bulk discount 10%
   (c) 400 items @ €46.50 each, Trade discount 20%, Bulk discount 15%
   (d) 100 items @ €120.00 each, Trade discount 25%, Bulk discount 5%.

4. A retailer buys a product @ €17 for each unit. She receives a trade discount of 25%. She also receives a bulk discount of 10% when she purchases in excess of 100 items at one time. Calculate how much she pays when she buys 200 units.

5. A retailer buys Christmas decorations in June @ €12 a lot. He receives a trade discount of 20%, a bulk discount of 10% when he buys more than 100 lots, a seasonal discount of 5% and an anticipation discount of 5% if the payment is more than ten days early. Calculate the cash paid if:
   (a) he buys 50 lots and pays 5 days early
   (b) he buys 160 lots and pays 15 days early
   (c) he buys 220 lots and pays 12 days early
   (d) he buys 130 lots and pays on the date due.

Revision Exercise 7.5

1. Work out the following trade discounts to two decimal places.
   (a) 20% of €2189
   (b) 25% of €6248.24
   (c) $33\frac{1}{3}$% of €984
   (d) 15% of €1688
   (e) $12\frac{1}{2}$% of €2899.98
   (f) 25% of €287.50

2. Work out the following cash discounts.
   (a) $2\frac{1}{2}$% of €80
   (b) 5% of €988
   (c) $2\frac{1}{2}$% of €28964
   (d) 3% of €297.64
   (e) 5% of €9998.24
   (f) $2\frac{1}{2}$% of €21 777.28

FOREIGN CURRENCY

Currency describes a unit of money in use in a country. Most countries have their own currency. When one currency is expressed in terms of another, this is known as the rate of exchange. Exchange rates are usually variable and depend on a number of factors. Exchange rates are quoted in most news sources (e.g. newspapers, radio, television and internet). The following is from the *Examiner* on Friday 31 December 1999:

	Euro			£Sterling	
	Euro	**Punt**		**Market Rate Day's Spread**	
US Dlr	1.0046	1.2756	Austria	22.1128–22.1458	22.1032–22.1967
Stg	0.62170	0.78940	Belgium	64.8262–64.9230	64.7980–65.0723
Jap yen	102.73	130.44	Canada	2.3393–2.3426	2.3393–2.3547
Swiss franc	1.6051	2.0381	Denmark	11.9600–11.9780	11.9520–12.0020
Gr drachma	330.30	419.39	Euro	1.6070–1.6094	1.6063–1.6131
Dan krone	7.4433	9.4510	France	10.5412–10.5570	10.5366–10.5812
Swed Krona	8.5625	10.8721	Germany	3.1430–3.1477	3.1416–3.1549
Nor krone	8.0765	10.2550	Holland	3.5414–3.5467	3.5398–3.5548
Czech Koruna	36.103	45.841	Italy	3111.58–3116.23	3110.23–3123.39
Cypriot Pound	0.57667	0.73222	Japan	164.88–165.13	164.59–165.62
Estonian kroon	15.6466	19.8671	Norway	12.9440–12.9660	12.9370–13.0300
Hungarian forint	254.70	323.40	Portugal	322.17–322.65	322.03–323.39
Polish zloty	4.1587	5.2805	Spain	267.38–267.78	267.26–268.39
Slov. tolar	198.90	252.55	Sweden	13.7490–13.7740	13.7300–13.8190
Can dollar	1.4608	1.8548	Swiss	2.5792–2.5841	2.5747–2.5896
Austra'ln dlr	1.5422	2.9582	US	1.6130–1.6140	1.6130–1.6206
New Zealand dollar	1.9357	2.4578			

Table 7.1   Foreign exchanges

This table shows for example that US$1.0046 = €1; that NZ$1.9357 = €1.

Changing euros to foreign currency

Example 12
Convert €100 to USA dollars. Rate of exchange (as in per Table 7.1) is US$1.0046.

Answer
Multiply the € by the exchange rate with US$.

€100 × 1.0046 = US$100.46

Example 13
Convert €220 to Japanese yen. Rate of exchange €1 = 102.73 yen.

Answer
Once again multiply the € by the exchange rate with Japanese yen.

€220 × 102.73
= 22 600.60 yen

Changing foreign currency to euros

Example 14

Change US$980 to €. Rate of exchange €1 = $1.0046.

Answer

Divide the dollars by the exchange rate with euros.

US$980 ÷ 1.0046

We must remove the decimal point by multiplying both numbers by 10 000

= 9 800 000 ÷ 10046
= €975.51

Example 15

Change 12 000 Japanese yen to €. Exchange rate €1 = 102.73 yen.

Answer

12 000 ÷ 102.73
= 1 200 000 ÷ 10273
= €116.81

Exercise 7.6

Note: For questions 1–12 use the exchange rates given in Figure 7.1 or find out the current exchange rate.

1. Convert €10 00 to US dollars.

2. Convert €5800 to Japanese yen.

3. Convert €780 to Swiss francs.

4. Convert €968 to Estonian kroon.

5. Convert €87 to Canadian dollars.

6. Convert US$1800 to euros.

7. Convert 9200 Japanese yen to euros.

8. Convert 9200 Swiss francs to euros.

9. Convert 8962 New Zealand dollars to euros.

10. Convert 8920 Canadian dollars to euros.

11. An Irish exporter sells goods to a company in Switzerland for 8600 Swiss francs. How much does she receive in euros?

12. An American tourist arrives in Ireland and converts US$1000 to €. After touring Ireland she intends to visit England. If she spends €700 while in Ireland, how much sterling will she get for the remainder?

13. (a) Change 10 900 Swiss francs to € when €1 = Swiss Fr. 1.70.
    (b) Change US$1260 to € when €1 = US$1.12.
    (c) Change 2760 Canadian dollars to € when €1 = 1.83 Canadian dollars.
    (d) Change 20 000 New Zealand dollars to € when €1 = NZ$2.01.
    (e) Change €20 000 to Japanese yen when €1 = 90.23.

THE EURO

The realisation of a single European currency dates back to the Maastrict Treaty. This lay down the foundation for greater European economic integration. The aim of the common currency is to facilitate trade within the EU between member states, removing the uncertainty caused by fluctuating exchange rates. Not all EU members are at present joined to the euro currency. Most notably for Irish exporters and importers the UK is not a member, although it is expected they may join in the future. The current members of the euro are as follows: Belgium, France, Germany, Ireland, Italy, Luxembourg, The Netherlands, Portugal and Spain.

The exchange rate between the IR£ and the € is:

€1 = IR£0.787564   (IR£0.79)
£1 = €1.269738   (€1.27)

CHAPTER 8

Calculations in relation to the operations of a business

In this chapter we will deal with:
— calculating compound interest
— use of the compound interest formula
— calculating insurance premiums
— calculating depreciation in two ways:
    (1) Straight line (fixed instalment) method
    (2) Diminishing balance method.

INTRODUCTION TO CALCULATING INTEREST

When a person invests a sum of money in a financial institution, he/she is paid for the use of this money. The money he/she is paid is called *interest*. The sum of money invested is called the *principal*. The interest paid is generally a percentage of the amount invested. This percentage is called the *rate*. Time is the length of time for which the investment is made. *Amount* is the principal plus the interest. Sometimes the investor withdraws the interest at the end of each year so that the amount of money invested remains the same from year to year.

Example 1

If a person invests €100 for 1 year at 10% interest, then he/she would receive €10 interest, i.e.

$$\tfrac{10}{100} \times €100 = €10 \text{ interest}$$

Example 2

The interest on €400 for 1 year at 10%

$$= \tfrac{10}{100} \times €400 = €40$$

Example 3

The interest on €400 for 2 years at 10%

$$= €400 \times 2 \times \tfrac{10}{100} = €80$$

Notice that the interest, i.e. €80 in Example 3, is obtained by multiplying the principal by the time by the rate and dividing by 100. This leads us to the formula:

$$\text{Interest} = \frac{\text{Principal} \times \text{Time} \times \text{Rate}}{100}$$

which is more usually written as:

$$I = \frac{P \times T \times R}{100}$$

This is the *simple interest formula*. Simple interest means that the interest is calculated on the original fixed principal and does not vary from year to year. It is paid directly to the investor. However, more usually, the investor will decide to leave the interest in the bank. In this case, the interest earned in the first year will be added on to the money invested and the combined amount will earn interest during the second year. This kind of interest is called *compound interest*.

COMPOUND INTEREST

The basic method for calculating compound interest is illustrated in the following examples.

Example 4

Find the compound interest on €1000 invested for 2 years at 10% per annum.

Answer

$$I = \frac{P \times T \times R}{100}$$

$$\text{Interest for first year} = \frac{1000 \times 1 \times 10}{100} = €100$$

Principal for the second year = €1000 + €100 = €1100

$$\text{Interest for second year} = \frac{1100 \times 1 \times 10}{100} = €110$$

Total compound interest for the two years is €100 + €110 = €210.

Example 5

Find what €2000 would amount to in 3 years, at 8% per annum.

Answer

$$I = \frac{P \times T \times R}{100}$$

Interest for first year $= \dfrac{2000 \times 1 \times 8}{100} = €160$

Principal for the second year $= €2000 + €160 = €2160$

Interest for second year $= \dfrac{2160 \times 1 \times 8}{100} = €172.80$

Principal for third year $= €2160 + €172.80 = €2332.80$

Interest for third year $= \dfrac{2332.80 \times 1 \times 8}{100} = €186.62$

Total interest $= €160 + €172.80 + €186.62 = €519.42$
Answer is $€519.42 + €2000 = €2519.42$

€2519.42 is what €2000 would amount to in 3 years at 8% per annum.

Example 6

You work for M. Jones Ltd. The company has €10 000 that it wants to invest. The Irish Financial Company is offering interest at 8% per annum. Your manager has asked you to calculate compound interest on the €10 000 at 8% p.a., $3\frac{1}{2}$ years after the original deposit is made.

Answer

$$I = \frac{P \times T \times R}{100}$$

	€
Principal for first year	10 000.00
Interest for first year $= \dfrac{10\,000 \times 1 \times 8}{100}$	800.00
Principal for second year	10 800.00
Interest for second year $= \dfrac{10\,800 \times 1 \times 8}{100}$	864.00
Principal for third year	11 664.00
Interest for third year $= \dfrac{11\,664 \times 1 \times 8}{100}$	933.12
Principal for fourth year	12 597.12
Interest for $\frac{1}{2}$ year $= \dfrac{12\,597.12 \times \frac{1}{2} \times 8}{100}$	503.88
Amount after $3\frac{1}{2}$ years	13 101.02

Compound interest after $3\frac{1}{2}$ years = €800.00 + €864.00 + €933.12 + €503.90 = €3101.02

Example 7

You have just been offered a job with R. O'Reilly Ltd. In order to get to work, you have to buy a car. You decide to borrow €6000 at a compound rate of 7% p.a. At the end of the first year, you estimate that you will repay €500 and at the end of the second year, €600. How much do you owe at the end of the second year?

Answer

$$I = \frac{P \times T \times R}{100}$$

	€
Principal for first year	6000.00
Interest for first year = $\dfrac{€6000 \times 1 \times 7}{100}$	420.00
Amount at end of year 1 = €6000 + €420 =	6420.00
Amount repaid in first year = less	500.00
Amount at end of year 1, less first repayment =	5920.00
Interest for second year = $\dfrac{€5900 \times 1 \times 7}{100}$ =	414.40
Amount at end of year 2 = €5920 + €414 =	6334.40
Amount repaid in second year = less	600.00
Amount at end of year 2, less second repayment =	5734.40

Answer is €5734.40 still owed at end of second year.

Exercise 8.1

In questions 1–6, find the compound interest, correct to two decimal places, where necessary:

1. €200 for 2 years at 7%

2. €800 for 2 years at 8%

3. €450 for 2 years at 6%

4. €2 900 for 3 years at 11%

5. €9240 for 3 years at 10%

6. €18940 for 3 years at 8%

7. Calculate to the nearest pound, the compound interest on €5200 for three years at 12%.

8. Mary Jones invests €10 000 for $2\frac{1}{2}$ years at 8%. Calculate the amount of compound interest after $2\frac{1}{2}$ years.

9. How much interest would a depositor receive at the end of 3 years if he was paid $12\frac{1}{2}$% p.a. compound interest on a deposit of €5000. Interest is paid half-yearly.

10. ABC Sporting Club places €9200 on deposit with the Bank of Ireland. A year later, a further €10 000 is placed on deposit. What will the total deposit amount to after 2 years and 10 months, at 10% per annum?

11. €8000 is placed on deposit at a bank at $7\frac{1}{2}$% p.a. compound interest. Eighteen months later, a further €5000 is deposited on the same terms. Calculate the compound interest payable on the total deposit after a total of three years.

12. Peter Murphy invests €800 for three years at compound interest rates. The rates for the three years are 10%, 8% and 5%, respectively. He withdraws €280 at the end of the first year and again at the end of the second year. What is left in his account at the end of the third year?

Compound interest formula

Sometimes compound interest is payable for a large number of years and using the method described in the previous section can become very confusing. Instead we can use a formula which is as follows:

$$A = P \times \left(1 + \frac{R}{100}\right)^n \quad \text{or for depreciation} \quad A = P \times \left(1 - \frac{R}{100}\right)^n$$

where A = Amount, P = Principal, R = Rate percentage and n = Number of years.
In the formula, the n outside the bracket means that the number inside must be multiplied by itself n times, e.g. $(1.6)^2 = 1.6 \times 1.6$.

Example 8

Margaret has invested €10 000 for 5 years at 6% per annum compound interest. What will the investment amount to at the end of five years?

Answer

$$A = P \times \left(1 + \frac{R}{100}\right)^n$$

$$= €10\,000 \times \left(1 + \frac{6}{100}\right)^5$$

$= 10\,000 \times (1.06)^5$
$= 10\,000 \times 1.3382255$
$= €13\,382.26$
$=$ investment at the end of five years

Exercise 8.2

1. Use the compound interest formula to calculate the amount that will accumulate in each of the following investments.

	Principal (€)	Rate of interest (p.a.)	Number of years
(a)	4000	6%	4
(b)	6000	8%	6
(c)	15 000	10%	7
(d)	21 000	$9\frac{1}{2}\%$	4

INSURANCE PREMIUMS

Insurance may be defined as protection against financial loss arising from something which may or may not happen, e.g. a factory burning down, a company motor vehicle being involved in a traffic accident, etc. As accidents like these do not befall everyone, the financial risk may be spread over all, at little relative cost to each.

Insurance companies, using statistical information gathered over long periods, are able to estimate the probability of a certain event happening and can then charge the appropriate amount (premium) for insurance.

For a company, the important types of insurance are: fidelity, guarantee, fire, burglary, public liability, employee liability and accident insurance.

Example 9

ABC Company annually takes out fire insurance for €50 000. The premium rate is 0.20%. How much is paid to the insurance company?

Answer

Method 1

The premium is 0.20% of €50 000. This means 20c in every €100.

$$\text{Therefore, premium} = \frac{€50\,000 \times 20c}{100}. \text{ Now cancel 100 into €50 000}$$

$$= €500 \times 20\,c$$
$$= €100$$

€100 is paid to the insurance company.

Method 2

(b) 1% of €50 000 = €500

$$0.20\% = \tfrac{1}{5} \text{ of } 1\% = \tfrac{1}{5} \times €500 = \frac{€500}{5} = €100$$

€100 is paid to the insurance company.

Note: The value of property is expressed in thousands rather than in hundreds of pounds. Therefore, insurance companies tend to quote premiums "per €1000" rather than "per €100".

Example 10

T. Jones Ltd insures his business against fire to the value of €40 000. How much will the insurance cost at a rate of €10.50 per €1000?

Answer

Find out how many times €1000 is contained in €40 000 and multiply by €10.50, i.e.

$$\frac{40\ 000 \times €10.50}{1000} = €420$$

€420 will be paid to the insurance company.

Example 11

Tom Kelly is a deep sea diver. His hobby is hang gliding. Tom works abroad for six months of the year. Tom is a non-smoker. His basic premium is €800. Calculate Tom's life assurance premium, taking into account that loadings are added for dangerous hobbies, dangerous occupations and living abroad. Deductions are given for being a non-smoker. Each loading is 10% of the basic premium and the deduction is 5% of the basic premium plus loadings.

Answer

	€	€
Basic premium		800
Add loadings:		
Occupation (10%)	80	
Hobby (10%)	80	
Living abroad (10%)	80	240
Subtotal (basic plus loadings)		1040
Less deduction non-smoker (5% of basic plus loadings)		52
Total premium to be paid		988

€988 is Tom's life assurance premium.

Example 12

Mary is a sales representative living in Dublin and is aged 20 years. She is seeking car insurance for the first time. She has a full driving licence and is a non-drinker. Her basic premium on her 1000 cubic capacity (cc) car is €500.

Loadings are 25% of the basic premium and deductions are 20% of the basic premium plus loadings.

Please note the following:

(i) Loadings are added for:
   - being under 25 years
   - first insurance
   - use of car for business.

(ii) Deductions are subtracted for:
   - having a full licence
   - being a non-drinker.

Calculate her car insurance premium.

Answer

	€	€
Basic premium		500
Add loadings:		
Sales representative – use of car	125	
Under 25	125	
First insurance	125	375
		875
Less deductions:	€	
Full licence	175	
Non-drinker I	175	350
Total premium to be paid		525

Exercise 8.3

1. Calculate the annual fire insurance premium for each of the following properties.
   - (a) Value of property €60 000, rate of premium €3 per €1000.
   - (b) Value of property €90 000, rate of premium €10 per €1000.
   - (c) Value of property €40 000, rate of premium €12 per €1000.
   - (d) Value of property €35 000, rate of premium €12.95 per €1000.
   - (e) Value of property €650 500, rate of premium €9.95 per €1000.

2. Calculate the premium rate per €1000 being charged in each of the following cases.
   - (a) Value of property €116 000, annual premium €284.
   - (b) Value of property €36 000, annual premium €360.
   - (c) Value of property €90 000, annual premium €225.
   - (d) Value of property €75 000, annual premium €900.

3. What is the total premium payable by a business person, if she insures her premises, valued at €50 000, for €10.95 per €1000, her stock, valued at €20 000, for €6.50 per €1000 and if she pays a fixed sum of €150 for public liability.

4. A business person is charged the following rates for fire insurance: €5.25 per €1000, for the first €40 000 of valuation and €5 per €1000 for the remainder. If the property is worth €100 000, what is the total annual premium?

5. Mary Jones pays €500 p.a. for fire insurance. This represents a rate of €5.60 per €1000 property valuation. What is the value of her property?

6. Calculate the *life assurance* premiums of the following people if *loadings* are: 20% of basic premiums for each of: dangerous occupations, medical conditions, living abroad. *Deductions* are 10% of basic plus loadings for each of – non-drinker, non-smoker, female.
   (a) Mary is a teacher in good health and does not drink or smoke. Basic Premium: €500.
   (b) Patricia is a teacher with a heart complaint. She drinks but does not smoke. Basic Premium: €700.
   (c) Patrick is a doctor who drinks and smokes. He also takes flying lessons. Basic Premium: €800.
   (d) Eileen is a steeplejack. She hang glides and works abroad. She is a non-smoker and a non-drinker. Basic Premium: €700.

7. Calculate the *car insurance premiums* of the following people if loadings and deductions are:
   Loadings: 25% of basic premium for first insurance, provisional licence, under 25 years, use of car for business, living in city.
   Deductions: 20% of basic premiums plus loadings for non-drinker, no claims bonus, full licence.
   (a) Breda is a sales representative from County Cork. She is aged 21 years. This is her first insurance. She is a non-drinker and has a full licence. Basic Premium: €1000.
   (b) Lil is a teacher from Carlow. She has a full licence, aged 25 years. She has a no claims bonus and is a non-drinker. Her basic premium is €400.
   (c) Larry is a 35-year-old sales representative, who lives in Dublin city. He has a full licence, is a non-drinker and has a full no claims bonus. His basic premium is €250.

8. Maureen aged 22 years is quoted a basic car insurance premium of €900. She must pay a 20% loading for her age. She is entitled to a 20% no claims bonus of the basic plus loading. She also requires comprehensive cover at €6.20 per €1000 on her €10 000 car. Calculate her premium.

9. Calculate the following house and contents premiums if the house premium is €5 per €1000 and the contents premium is €8 per €1000.
   (a) House value €50 000, contents value €15 000.
   (b) House value €100 000, contents value €30 000.
   (c) House value €65 000, contents value €20 000.

10. ABC Company annually takes out fire insurance for €50 000. The premium rate is 20%. How much is paid to the insurance company?

DEPRECIATION

Depreciation is a reduction in the value of a fixed asset of a business, due to wear and tear, use and age. A business usually reserves some of its profits annually in order to replace such fixed assets. The amount retained will depend on the estimated expected life of the asset. The trade-in or saleable value of the asset may also be taken into consideration, when determining the amount to be written off the asset each year.

There are two main methods of calculating depreciation:

1. straight line or fixed instalment method

2. diminishing (reducing) balance method.

1. Straight line or fixed instalment method of calculating depreciation

This method of calculating depreciation involves deducting a *fixed amount* each year during the life span of the asset.

Example 13

A company purchased a machine for €9000 with a life span of 3 years. It is estimated that it will have a trade-in value of €1500. Calculate the book value of the asset after 2 years, using the straight line method.

Answer

Note: divide (the original value less the estimated trade-in amount) by the expected life to find the amount to be written off each year.

Total amount to be written off: = €9000 − €1500 = €7500

Annual amount to be written off: $\dfrac{€7500}{3}$ = €2500

	€
Value – Year 1	9000
Depreciation – Year 1	2500
Value – Year 2	6500
Depreciation – Year 2	2500
Book Value – End of Year 2	4000

Answer: €4000 is the book value of the asset after 2 years.

Example 14

A motor van purchased for €10 000 in December 1990 is traded in for a new van in December 1993. If the depreciation is 25% p.a. on the fixed instalment method, how much can the owner expect to get against a new van?

Answer

Annual depreciation = 25% of €10 000 = €2 500

	€
Value – Year 1 (December 1990)	10 000
Depreciation – Year 1	2 500
Value – Year 2	7 500
Depreciation – Year 2 (December 1991)	2 500
Value – Year 3	5 000
Depreciation – Year 3 (December 1992)	2 500
Expected Trade-in Value (December 1993)	2 500

Answer: Expected Trade-in Value = €2500 (December 1993)

2. Diminishing (reducing balance) method

This means that a fixed percentage is written off the new diminished book value of the asset each year.

Example 15

A machine purchased for €10 000 in January 1990 was traded-in for a new machine in January 1993. If the depreciation is 25% p.a. on the diminishing balance method, how much can the owner expect to get against the new machine?

Answer

	€
Value – Year 1 (January 1990)	10 000.00
Depreciation – Year 1 (25% of €10 000)	2 500.00
Value – Year 2 (January 1991)	7 500.00
Depreciation – Year 2 (25% of €7500)	1 875.00
Value – Year 3 (January 1992)	5 625.00
Depreciation – Year 3 (25% of €5625)	1 406.25
Expected Trade-in Value (January 1993)	4 218.75

Answer: Expected Trade-in Value = €4218.75 (January 1993)

Example 16

ABC Company purchased a new computer for €2000 on 1 January 1993. It was decided to depreciate the computer at a rate of 10% p.a. on the diminishing balance method. A year later, 1 January 1994, a second computer was purchased for €2500 and it was decided to depreciate it in the same way. What was the book value of these computers on 31 December 1995?

Answer

	€
Value of computer – Year 1 (January 1993)	2 000
Depreciation – Year 1 (10% of €2000)	200
Value of computer – Year 2 (January 1994)	1 800
Add new computer (January 1994)	2 500
Total value of two computers (January 1994)	4 300
Depreciation (10% of €4300)	430
Value of computers (January 1995)	3 870
Depreciation (10% of €3870)	387
Book value of computers (December 1995)	3 483

Answer: Book value of computers (December 1995) = €3483

Exercise 8.4

1. Calculate the book value of the following assets after 3 years, if they are depreciated at the rates shown, using the fixed instalment method.

	Asset	Original value (€)	Rate (%)
(a)	Motor van	Cost 9 000	Depreciated at 10 p.a.
(b)	Computer	Cost 3 000	Depreciated at 25 p.a.
(c)	Machine	Cost 19 000	Depreciated at 10 p.a.
(d)	Buildings	Cost 150 000	Depreciated at 8 p.a.

2. What is the book value of the following assets after 3 years, if they are depreciated at the rates shown, using the diminishing balance method?

	Asset	Original value (€)	Rate (%)
(a)	Furniture	Cost 5 000	Depreciated at 10 p.a.
(b)	Buildings	Cost 90 000	Depreciated at 7 p.a.
(c)	Machine	Cost 15 000	Depreciated at $8\frac{1}{2}$ p.a.
(d)	Computers	Cost 6 000	Depreciated at 25 p.a.

3. A lorry is purchased for €18 000. Depreciation is reckoned at 12% p.a. on the fixed instalment method. How much would the book value of the lorry be after three years, if the diminishing balance method were used?

4. A motor van is purchased for €12 000, has an expected life of 5 years and an estimated scrap value of €2000. The machine is to be depreciated by the straight line method. Show the calculations for the first three years.

5. T. Twomey Ltd purchased a new machine on 1 January 1990 for €20 000. It is depreciated by 20% p.a. on the diminishing balance method. Show the calculations for the first four years.

6. P. Jones Ltd purchased a motor van on 1 January 1994 for €20 000. It was decided to depreciate the motor van by 15% p.a. on the diminishing balance method. A year later a second motor van was purchased for €15 000 and depreciated in the same way. What was the book value of these motor vans on 1 January 1997?

CHAPTER 9

Sample questions and assignments

In this chapter we will deal with:
— sample examination type questions
— sample business calculations assignments.

Question 9.1

Use of a calculator is NOT allowed.
Answer all of this section.
Express answers correct to 2 decimal places.

1. Calculate
   (a) $21\,854 + 6872 - 289$
   (b) $106.59 - 96.47$

2. Calculate $59\,874 \div 21$

3. Calculate 6294×625

4. Add $\frac{1}{2} + \frac{2}{3} + \frac{4}{6}$

5. Calculate $\frac{5}{6} + \frac{3}{4} - \frac{1}{3}$

6. Multiply
   (a) $\frac{2}{3} \times 1\frac{3}{8} \times \frac{3}{4}$
   (b) 157.89125

7. Divide $5\frac{1}{3} \div 1\frac{5}{6}$

8. Express in decimal form
   (a) $\frac{3}{5}$
   (b) $\frac{1}{3}$

9. Divide
   (a) 81.27 in the ratio of $7:2$
   (b) $271.744 \div 31.6$

10. Add
    (a) 21.75
        160.64
        2168.34
        300.04
    (b) If 5% discount amounts to €1.50, what is the total amount?

Question 9.2

Use of a calculator is allowed.
Answer all questions.
Express answers correct to 2 decimal places.

1. $145 \times 23 \times 426$

2. $26.3 \times 45.7 \times 20.3$

3. $\dfrac{87.6 \times 45.9}{2.4 \times 4.36}$

4. 15% of a sum of money is €2000. What is the sum of money?

5. $874 - (28.5\%$ of $260)$

6. A number is increased by 25%. If the new number is 4634, what was the original number?

7. A drum of petrol costs €324.90. A similar size drum of diesel oil costs $\frac{5}{9}$ of this price. Find the cost of the drum of oil.

8. The cost of a washing machine is €250. The selling price is €450. Find the percentage profit (expressed as percentage of cost).

9. A bankrupt owes his creditors €4800. He can only pay 35 cents in the euro. How much will his creditors receive altogether?

10. 14 people share a sum of €437.50 equally. How much does each receive?

Question 9.3

You are a secretarial student on work experience with Jones plc. The company has a square park with sides 25 m long. In it are four triangular flower beds. The base of each of these is 10 m long and the perpendicular height is 7 m. Grass is to be grown on the rest.

(a) Calculate the area of the park.

(b) Calculate the total area of the flower beds.

(c) Calculate the area that is to be set in grass.

(d) How much grass seed will be required if the quantity to be set is 1 kg per 50 m^2? Answer to the nearest kg.

(e) Calculate how much it will cost to set the grass, if the seed costs €3 per kg.

Question 9.4

Ann earns €255 per week net. Her weekly expenses are:

Rent €55
Groceries $\frac{1}{3}$ of her earnings
ESB €10
Insurance policy €8
Entertainment €25
Bus fares €15
Remainder in savings

(a) Calculate
  (i) her groceries
  (ii) her savings.

(b) Draft her weekly budget.

(c) Ann is due an increase in net pay of 8% and is considering the purchase of a second-hand car.
She reckons her petrol costs would be one and a half times her present bus fare costs. What repayments could she afford to make per week if her other expenses did not increase and she reduced her level of savings by $33\frac{1}{3}$%?

Question 9.5

Fifty secretarial students completed an office procedures test. The results, expressed in percentages, are shown in this frequency table.

Score	10	20	30	40	50	60	70	80	90	100
No. of students	4	2	8	11	10	5	3	4	2	1

(a) Calculate the mean score.

(b) What is the mode of the data?

(c) If 40% is a pass, how many candidates passed?

(d) What percentage of the candidates failed?

Question 9.6

Mary Jones works as a secretary in Portlaoise Computers plc.
She earns a basic wage of €120 per 40 hour week. She is paid time and a half for overtime and gets 20% of her weekly basic pay as an added bonus this week. Her tax free allowance is €65 per week.
She pays tax at 27% and PRSI on her gross earnings at 12.20%. If Mary works 8 hours overtime this week:

(a) Calculate her gross pay.

(b) Calculate her taxable pay.

(c) Calculate her PRSI contribution.

(d) Calculate her tax for the week.

(e) Calculate her take home pay.

Question 9.7

The management team of Murray's Confectioners plc are planning an Easter sales campaign. They have decided to market a specially wrapped gift pack of a variety of the company's products.
The pack will contain:

Items	Weight	Cost
1 box of luxury chocolates	907 g	€2.80 per box
2 sticks of hard-boiled rock	227 g per stick	€0.70 per stick
6 sticks of barley sugar	57 g per stick	€0.10 per stick
1 tin of butterscotch	454 g	€0.85 per tin

The cost of additional packaging including the box will amount to €2. 40% will be added to the total cost including packaging to obtain the selling price exclusive of VAT.
As a Sales Clerk you are asked to calculate the following:

(a) Calculate the total weight of the contents of the pack in kg.

(b) Calculate the total cost of the pack including the additional cost of packaging.

(c) Add 40% to the total cost (the answer from (b)) to obtain the selling price exclusive of VAT.

(d) If VAT is at 20%, calculate the selling price inclusive of VAT.

(e) Murray's Confectioners also wish to have this sales campaign in America. Convert the selling price (the answer in (d)) into dollars, giving your answer correct to 2 decimal places (€1 = US$1.05).

Question 9.8

You work as an Accounts Assistant in Jones Ltd. The company purchased a van for €10 000 in May 2000. In May 2003 it is to be traded in for a new van. Your manager has asked you to calculate the following:

(a) If the depreciation is at 20% p.a. on the diminishing balance method, the manager wants you to calculate how much the company can expect to get against the new van.

(b) The manager has also asked you to calculate how much the company will earn if it invests €2500 for three years at 8.5% compound interest.

BUSINESS CALCULATIONS

Sample assignment 1

Two German business consultants are visiting Moran (Irl) Ltd Dublin from Monday 7 November 2001 until Friday 11 November 2001.
You have been asked by your manager to obtain the following information:

(a) Choose three hotels in the area and find the total cost for accommodation for five nights for the two business people.

(b) If dinner was included for three evenings how much would that cost?

(c) Select a hotel and give a reason why.

(d) At current rates what would be the cost of each hotel in Deutschmarks? (Please state the exchange rate and the date and the place where the exchange rate was obtained.)

Sample assignment 2

You work with Dooley Computers plc. The management have decided to completely redecorate the reception area, i.e. to re-paper and re-carpet the area. The floor measures 6 m long by 3 m wide. The walls have a height of 6 m. Please note the total area of the doors is 8 m². The management are willing to pay approximately €6 per roll for wallpaper and approximately €8 per metre of carpet.
You are requested to:

(a) Get costings from at least three wallpaper shops.

(b) Get costings from at least three carpet shops.

(c) Choose one quotation from the wallpaper shops and one from the carpet shops and outline the total cost to the company of the redecoration.

(d) Include, in your assignment, details of the VAT charges for each item.

Sample assignment 3

You have won a sum of money, €50 000 in the Lotto. You now have to decide how to invest the money. You have many options open to you.

Requirement

Choose three options open to you as to how to invest the money. Visit the banks/financial institutions selected and find out the interest per annum given in each case. Include, in your assignment, the compound interest that your money will earn in two years. (Assume that you leave the money in the institution for two years.)

CHAPTER 10
Solutions

CHAPTER 1

Exercise 1.1
1. (a) $1\frac{1}{6}$
   (b) $1\frac{5}{12}$
   (c) $\frac{13}{15}$
   (d) $1\frac{23}{40}$
   (e) $2\frac{19}{40}$
   (f) $1\frac{20}{21}$

2. (a) $18\frac{13}{18}$
   (b) $10\frac{3}{8}$
   (c) $12\frac{1}{3}$
   (d) $12\frac{1}{4}$
   (e) $19\frac{3}{10}$
   (f) $14\frac{4}{9}$

Exercise 1.2
1. (a) $\frac{5}{9}$
   (b) $\frac{11}{24}$
   (c) $\frac{7}{24}$
   (d) $\frac{17}{30}$
   (e) $\frac{1}{8}$
   (f) $\frac{4}{15}$

2. (a) $\frac{1}{5}$
   (b) $1\frac{5}{11}$
   (c) $5\frac{9}{10}$
   (d) $3\frac{3}{40}$
   (e) $3\frac{7}{20}$
   (f) $7\frac{22}{35}$

Exercise 1.3
1. (a) $\frac{1}{4}$
   (b) $\frac{15}{56}$
   (c) $\frac{7}{30}$
   (d) $\frac{5}{24}$
   (e) $\frac{17}{64}$
   (f) $\frac{7}{10}$

2. (a) $\frac{63}{121}$
   (b) $\frac{256}{357}$
   (c) $\frac{9}{56}$
   (d) $\frac{57}{140}$
   (e) $\frac{7}{40}$
   (f) $\frac{11}{36}$

Exercise 1.4
1. (a) $8\frac{1}{3}$
   (b) $114\frac{3}{14}$
   (c) $8\frac{3}{4}$
   (d) $14\frac{7}{27}$
   (e) $9\frac{3}{62}$
   (f) $15\frac{1}{2}$
   (g) $14\frac{13}{28}$

Exercise 1.5

1. (a) 2
   (b) $\frac{19}{81}$
   (c) $\frac{64}{121}$
   (d) 1
   (e) $1\frac{25}{52}$
   (f) $\frac{440}{589}$

2. (a) $\frac{40}{57}$
   (b) $12\frac{5}{9}$
   (c) $\frac{804}{889}$
   (d) $\frac{49}{72}$
   (e) $1\frac{31}{57}$
   (f) $4\frac{4}{9}$

Exercise 1.6

1. (a) 3
   (b) 120
   (c) 50
   (d) 2

Exercise 1.7

1. (a) $\frac{11}{20}$
   (b) $11\frac{7}{27}$
   (c) $1\frac{37}{48}$
   (d) $80\frac{1}{5}$
   (e) $21\frac{89}{384}$

Exercise 1.8

1. (a) $\frac{6}{10}$
   (b) $\frac{6}{100}$
   (c) $\frac{6}{1000}$
   (d) $\frac{6}{10}$

2. (a) $\frac{3}{5}$
   (b) $\frac{7}{10}$
   (c) $\frac{3}{50}$
   (d) $\frac{7}{1000}$
   (e) $1\frac{1}{2}$
   (f) $\frac{4}{25}$

3. (a) 0.6
   (b) 0.07
   (c) 0.004
   (d) 0.12
   (e) 0.021
   (f) 4.1

Exercise 1.9

1. (a) 123.91
   (b) 210.61
   (c) 155.048
   (d) 2339.934
   (e) 4974.452
   (f) 4596.276

2. (a) 3.45
   (b) 23.22
   (c) 120.811
   (d) 995.464
   (e) 32 883.218
   (f) 9679.544

Exercise 1.10

1. (a) 14.322
   (b) 58.305
   (c) 2731.32
   (d) 250.3614
   (e) 28.014
   (f) 66604.4
   (g) 379.288
   (h) 392.494128
   (i) 1634.509

Exercise 1.11

1. (a) 627
   (b) 429.76
   (c) 6291
   (d) 12 852.68
   (e) 12 942
   (f) 26 748

2. (a) 6.297
   (b) 6.9724
   (c) 0.69724
   (d) 29.82
   (e) 0.06724
   (f) 19.761

Exercise 1.12

1. (a) 64.70
   (b) 157.36
   (c) 105.99
   (d) 1.09

2. (a) 1.56
   (b) 12.48
   (c) 16.96
   (d) 69.50
   (e) 518.84
   (f) 336.64
   (g) 12.33
   (h) 22.55
   (i) 42.62

Exercise 1.13

1. (a) 62.5%
   (b) 75%
   (c) 40%
   (d) 112.5%
   (e) 10%
   (f) 12.5%
   (g) 6.25%
   (h) 137.5%
   (i) 587.5%
   (j) 850%
   (k) 440%

2. (a) 52%
   (b) 125%
   (c) 67.89%
   (d) 627%
   (e) 296.78%
   (f) 25.6%
   (g) 97.6%
   (h) 287%

Exercise 1.14

1. (a) $\frac{1}{5}$
   (b) $\frac{1}{2}$
   (c) $\frac{14}{25}$
   (d) $\frac{12}{25}$
   (e) $\frac{109}{400}$
   (f) $\frac{4}{5}$
   (g) $\frac{7}{30}$
   (h) $\frac{137}{1100}$
   (i) $1\frac{6}{25}$

2. (a) 0.27
   (b) 0.0927
   (c) 0.64
   (d) 0.6666
   (e) 0.78
   (f) 0.21
   (g) 0.45
   (h) 0.13
   (i) 0.1872

Exercise 1.15

1. (a) 26%
   (b) 5%
   (c) 20%
   (d) 75%
   (e) 64%
   (f) 0.33%
   (g) 3.7%
   (h) 5.83%
   (i) 64.29%

Exercise 1.16

1. (a) 193.6
   (b) 27.6
   (c) 986
   (d) 26 786.7
   (e) €73.80
   (f) €185.50
   (g) €2 463.45
   (h) €14.70
   (i) 2.88
   (j) €69
   (k) 78.2
   (l) €55.20

2. (a) 249.6 kg
   (b) 12.5 km
   (c) 1800 litres
   (d) 435 litres
   (e) 320 km
   (f) 84.39 litres
   (g) 162 kg
   (h) 76.2 km

Exercise 1.17

1. 500

2. 800

3. 2000

4. 852

5. 930

6. 238

7. 4571.43

8. 7.5%

Revision Exercise 1.18

1. 1160

2. €428.57

3. 45%

4. 53.33%

5. 13.64%, €82.50

6. 16.67%

CHAPTER 2

Exercise 2.1

1. (a) 189
   (b) 179

2. 68

3. (a) 108
   (b) 54

4. 56

5. €875

6. €532

4. 800

5. 103.50

6. 5472

7. 12.821

8. 28%

9. 205 298 884

10. 1 229 821.5

11. 5.77

12. €607.69

13. 99.75

14. 6100

Exercise 2.2

1. 190 563 392

2. 76 325.37

3. 13.90

15. 6.188

16. 11.76%

17. 137 774 324

18. 50 566.20

19. 8.81

20. €550

21. 120

22. 7050

23. 1.95

24. 6%

CHAPTER 3

Exercise 3.1

1. (a) 460 mm
   (b) 400 mm
   (c) 40 mm
   (d) 6000 mm
   (e) 850 mm

2. (a) 60 cm
   (b) 45.5 cm
   (c) 7000 cm
   (d) 300 cm
   (e) 72 cm

3. (a) 4.9 m
   (b) 5.5 m
   (c) 60 m
   (d) 5.6 m
   (e) 3000 m
   (f) 400 m

4. 780 km

5. (a) 4 300 mm^2
   (b) 5 200 000 mm^2
   (c) 340 000 mm^2

6. (a) 32 cm^2
   (b) 350 000 cm^2
   (c) 4 500 cm^2

7. (a) 490 000 m^2
   (b) 5 000 000 m^2
   (c) 2.5 m^2
   (d) 9 700 m^2
   (e) 3.56 m^2
   (f) 4.7 m^2

8. 36 km

9. (a) 30 cm^2
   (b) 32 m^2
   (c) 100 dam^2
   (d) 30 mm^2

10. (a) 1555 m^2
    (b) 1060 cm^2
    (c) 106.5 m^2

11. (a) 19 m^2
    (b) 21 m^2

12. (a) 286.5 m^2
    (b) 242.8 m^2

13. (a) 48 cm^2
    (b) 21 mm^2
    (c) 5 m^2
    (d) 3 cm^2 or 300 mm^2
    (e) 52.5 cm^2

14. (a) 154 cm^2
    (b) 616 m^2
    (c) 44 506 mm^2
    (d) 3 850 cm^2
    (e) 346.5 dam^2
    (f) 86.625 m^2

15. (a) 4 224 cm^2
    (b) 4 092 m^2
    (c) 2 013 mm^2
    (d) 22 176 cm^2
    (e) 7.48 m^2 or 74 800 cm^2
    (f) 7.2468 m^2 or 72 468 cm^2

16. 437.5 m^2

17. (a) 25 mats
    (b) 1050 cm^2

18. (a) 86.5 m^2
    (b) 513.5 m^2

Exercise 3.2

1. (a) 3 560 000 cm^3
   (b) 3 500 000 000 cm^3
   (c) 5 875 606 cm^3
   (d) 461 724 000 cm^3 or 461.724 m^3
   (e) 2 920 litres
   (f) 49 000 cm^3

2. (a) 182.49 m^3
   (b) 1282.6 cm^3
   (c) 184.275 m^3

3. 9387 litres
   6101.55 litres

4. (a) 163.28 cm^3
   (b) 269.255 m^3
   (c) 0.589 m^3

5. 2.94 m^3

6. (a) 523.3 cm^3
   (b) 0.785 m^3
   (c) 51 054.3 cm^3
   (d) 16.7 m^3
   (e) 10 381.6 cm^3

7. 209.33 minutes

8. (a) 155 m^2
   (b) 6.925 m^2
   (c) 148.075 m^2
   (d) 3 kg
   (e) €6.00

9. 30 people

Exercise 3.3

1. 3.976 litres

2. 15925 millilitres

3. 93.98 cm

4. 139.7 cm

5. 1.78 m

6. 5.3 m

7. 81.78 km

8. 16 200 ares

9. 158.84 m^2

10. 0.93 m^2

11. 35.145 cm^2

12. 8 000 cm^3

13. 198.59 g

14. 2.44 kg

15. €35.20

Exercise 3.4

1. Mary – €10
   Helen – €20
   Liam – €10
   Alan – €10

2. John – €103.50
   Paul – €172.50
   David – €69
   Elaine – €207
   Gavin – €138

3. Olive – €90
   Anne – €30
   Suzanne – €180

4. Comp. 1 – 574.08 kg
   Comp. 2 – 1148.16 kg
   Comp. 3 – 669.76 kg

5. 125 : 93

6. 100 : 1

7. 1 : 48

8. (a) 196 : 1
   (b) 14 : 1

9. (a) $\frac{1}{30}$
   (b) 0.03

10. 0.059

11. $x = 5$

12. $x = 81$

13. $x = 51$

14. $x = 44$

15. 420 km

16. 504 units

17. 8 km

18. 0.82 km

19. (a) 21 : 1
    (b) 48.3 mm, 88.2 mm

20. 16.25 cm

Exercise 3.5

1. 16.10

2. 14.10

3. 5.19 pm

4. 3.49 am

5. 10.15 am

6. 6 hours

7. 8.28 am
   4 hours 13 minutes

CHAPTER 4

Exercise 4.1

1. (a) Mary €824
      June €1236
      James €1030
   (b) James €130
      Breda €364
      Maureen €50.70
      Lil €81.58

2. Mortgage €420
   Car insurance €630
   ESB €52.50
   Car tax €94.50

3. Budget for Murray household for first 4 months of 1997

	January (€)	February(€)	March (€)	April (€)	Total
Income					
P. Murray	1000	1000	1000	1000	4000
M. Murray	1200	1200	1200	1200	4800
Child benefit	40	40	40	40	160
1 Total income	2 240	2 240	2 240	2 240	8 960
Expenditure					
Fixed					
Car insurance	–	600	–	–	600
Car tax	100	–	–	–	100
Car loan repayments	300	300	300	300	1200
House mortgage	300	300	300	300	1200
House insurance	–	–	100	–	100
2 Subtotal	700	1200	700	600	3200
Irregular					
ESB bill	–	100	–	80	180
Petrol costs	80	80	80	80	320
Household expenses	200	200	200	200	800
3 Subtotal	280	380	280	360	1 300
Discretionary					
Entertainment	50	50	50	50	200
Birthday expenses	–	80	80	–	160
4 Subtotal	50	130	130	50	360
5 Total expenditure (2 + 3 + 4)	1030	1710	1110	1010	4860
6 Net cash (1 − 5)	1210	530	1130	1230	4100
7 Opening cash	100	1310	1840	2970	100
Closing cash (6 + 7)	1310	1840	2970	4200	4200

4. Budget for Briody family for first 4 months of 1997

	January (€)	February(€)	March (€)	April (€)	Total
Income					
Paul Briody	1200	1200	1200	1200	4800
Kathleen Briody	1300	1300	1300	1300	5200
Child benefit	60	60	60	60	240
1 Total income	2 560	2 560	2 560	2 560	10 240
Expenditure					
Fixed					
House mortgage	350	350	350	350	1 400
Car tax	150	–	–	–	150
Car insurance	–	–	450	–	450
2 Subtotal	500	350	800	350	2000
Irregular					
Groceries	250	250	250	250	1000
ESB bill	70	–	50	–	120
Telephone bill	–	100	–	90	190
Car running costs	100	145	100	100	445
3 Subtotal	420	495	400	440	1755
Discretionary					
Entertainment	60	60	60	60	240
Birthday	–	50	–	–	50
4 Subtotal	60	110	60	60	290
5 Total expenditure (2 + 3 + 4)	980	955	1260	850	4045
6 Net cash (1 − 5)	1580	1605	1300	1710	6195
7 Opening cash	90	1670	3275	4575	90
Closing cash (6 + 7)	1670	3275	4575	6285	6285

5. Kavanagh family budget for June, July, August and September 1997

	June (€)	July (€)	August (€)	September (€)	Total
Income					
T. Kavanagh	900	900	1100	900	3800
M. Kavanagh	800	816	816	816	3248
1 Total income	1700	1716	1916	1716	7048
Expenditure					
Fixed					
Mortgage	400	400	400	400	1600
Car tax	–	100	–	–	100
2 Subtotal	400	500	400	400	1700
Irregular					
Groceries	300	300	300	300	1200
ESB bill	60	–	50	–	110
Telephone bill	100	–	160	–	260
3 Subtotal	460	300	510	300	1570
Discretionary					
Entertainment	50	50	50	50	200
Birthdays	–	80	–	–	80
4 Subtotal	50	130	50	50	280
5 Total expenditure (2 + 3 + 4)	910	930	960	750	3550
6 Net cash (1 − 5)	790	786	956	966	3498
7 Opening cash	200	990	1776	2732	200
Closing cash (6 + 7)	990	1776	2732	3698	3698

6. (a) Caroline €290 per week
Groceries = $\frac{1}{3}$ of €290 = €290 ÷ 3 = €96.67

(b) (i) *Income*   €290.00
Expenditure

Rent	70.00	
Groceries	96.67	
ESB	12.00	
Insurance	8.00	
Entertainment	35.00	
Bus fares	12.00	233.67

(ii) *Savings*   €56.33

(c) Increase 7% New income €290 + 7% = 290 + 20.30 = €310.30

$$\frac{7}{100} \times 290 = \frac{203}{10} = 20.30$$

Petrol €12 + $\frac{1}{2}$ = €12 + €6 = €18

Savings €56.33 − 50% = $56.33 - \frac{28.161}{2}$ = €28.17

Expected Income   €310.30
Expenditure

Rent	70.00	
Groceries	96.67	
ESB	12.00	
Insurance	8.00	
Entertainment	35.00	
Petrol	18.00	
Savings	28.17	267.84

Repayments   42.46

(d) *Balancing budget*
Income   €310.30

Rent	70.00	
Groceries	96.67	
ESB	12.00	
Insurance	8.00	
Entertainment	35.00	
Petrol	18.00	
Savings	28.17	
Repayments	42.46	310.30

Balance   NIL

7. (a) Tom earns €350 per week.
Groceries $= \frac{1}{4}$ of earnings $= \frac{1}{4}$ of €350 = €87.50

(b)
Earnings		€350.00
Expenditure		
Mortgage	90.00	
Groceries	87.50	
ESB	10.00	
Car	20.00	
Entertainment	40.00	247.50
Savings		€102.50

Increase 3% = $^{7}350 \times \dfrac{3}{\underset{2}{100}} = \dfrac{21}{2}$ = €10.50

New income €350 + €10.50 = €360.50
Savings $\frac{1}{3}$ less 102.50 ÷ 3 = €34.17
€102.50 − €34.17 = €68.33
Entertainment less 20% = $\frac{1}{5}\frac{1}{5}$ of 40.00 = €8.00
€40.00 − €8.00 = €32.00

Expected income		€360.50
Expenditure		
Mortgage	90.00	
Groceries	87.50	
ESB	10.00	
Car	20.00	
Entertainment	32.00	
Savings	68.33	€307.87
Repayments		52.67

(d)
Balancing budget		
Income		€360.50
Expenditure		
Mortgage	90.00	
Groceries	87.50	
ESB	10.00	
Car	20.00	
Entertainment	32.00	
Savings	68.33	
Repayments	52.67	€360.50
Balance		NIL

8. (a) Helen earns €290 per week
        Groceries = $\frac{1}{4}$ of €290 = €72.50

   (b) (i) *Income*   €290.00
            Expenditure
            Rent   75.00
            Groceries   72.50
            ESB   11.00
            Entertainment   35.00
            Bus fares   20.00   213.50
            _____

        (ii) *Savings*   €76.50

   (c) New income €290 + 8% = 290 × $\frac{8}{100}$ = $\frac{232}{10}$ = €23.20
        €290 + €23.20 = €313.20
        Petrol 20 × $1\frac{1}{2}$ = 20 + 10 = €30
        Repairs and maintenance €20 €30 + €20 = €50
        Savings €76.50 − 25% = 76.50 − 19.13 = €57.37

        Expected income   313.20
        Expenditure
        Rent   75.00
        Groceries   72.50
        ESB   11.00
        Entertainment   35.00
        Petrol and car   50.00
        Savings   57.37   300.87
        _____

        Repayments   12.33

   (d) *Balancing budget*
       Income   €313.20
       Expenditure
       Rent   75.00
       Groceries   72.50
       ESB   11.00
       Entertainment   35.00
       Petrol and car   50.00
       Savings   57.37
       Repayments   12.33   313.20
       _____

       Balance   NIL

CHAPTER 5

Exercise 5.1

1. mean : 4.875
   mode : 5
   median : 5

2. mean : 16
   mode : 16
   median : 16

3. mean : 9
   mode : 9
   median : 9

4. mean : 45
   mode : 46
   median : 45.5

5. mean : 17
   mode : 17
   median : 17

6. mean : 28
   mode : 28
   median : 28

7. mean : 59
   mode : 59
   median : 59

8. mean : 33.2
   mode : 33
   median : 33

9. mean : 69.5
   mode : 70
   median : 70

10. mean : 13.5
    mode : 14
    median : 14

11. mean : 35.2
    mode : 36
    median : 36

12. mean : 2.1
    mode : 2

Exercise 5.2

1.

No.	31	32	33	34	35	36	37	38	39	40
Frequency	1	2	1	3	5	2	2	1	1	1

2.

No.	1	2	3	4	5	6	7	8	9	10	11	13
Frequency	1	2	1	2	2	4	2	2	1	1	1	1

3.

No. of Patrons	275–284	285–294	295–304	305–314	315–324	325–334	335–344
Frequency	1	2	0	2	4	4	10

No. of Patrons	345–354	355–364
Frequency	9	4

(a) 335 patrons per hour
(b) €1 340 per hour

4.

No.	47	49	51	52	53	54	55	57
Frequency	1	1	2	4	3	1	1	1

mode : 52
mean : 52.2

5.

No.	59	60	61	63	64	65	66	67	68	69	71
Frequency	1	1	1	1	3	2	3	2	2	1	1

mode : 64, 66
mean : 65.2

6.

No.	1	2	3	4	5	6	7	8
Frequency	2	2	2	4	2	2	2	2

mode : 4
mean : 4.4

7.

No.	51	52	53	54	55	56	57	58	59	61
Frequency	1	2	1	1	2	2	4	3	1	1

mode : 57
mean : 55.9

8.

No.	83	84	85	86	87	88	89	90	91	92	94
Frequency	1	2	1	2	2	6	3	2	1	1	1

mode : 88
mean : 87.9

9.

No.	12	13	14	15	16	17
Frequency	3	3	6	5	5	3

mode : 14
mean : 14.6

10.

No.	25	26	27	28	29	30	31	32	33	34
Frequency	1	2	3	3	7	5	4	1	1	1

mode : 29
mean : 29.2

11.	Interval	40–49	50–59	60–69	70–79	80–89
	Frequency	4	4	7	7	3

mean : 64.9

12.	Wages (IR£)	90–99	100–109	110–119	120–129	130–139	140–149
	Frequency	2	4	4	6	2	2

mean : IR£118.50

Exercise 5.3

9. Fianna Fáil – 45%
   Fine Gael – 30%
   Labour – 15%
   P.D. – 5%
   None – 5%

10. Food – €75
    Rent – €58.33

11. Interval	Frequency
10–20	10
20–30	15
30–50	45
50–70	55
70–100	37.5

12. Interval	Frequency
0–20	2
20–40	4
40–50	7
50–60	4
60–70	3
70–100	6

CHAPTER 6

Exercise 6.1

1. A: €132.16
   B: €174.64
   C: €184.08
   D: €212.40
   E: €165.20
   F: €233.64

2. 11: €139.20
   12: €238.50
   13: €153
   14: €165.75
   15: €201.60
   16: €158.40
   17: €144

3. 21: €262.50
   22: €225.55
   23: €217.00
   24: €262.50
   25: €215.14
   26: €208
   27: €262.50

4. C00102: €210.60
   C00103: €247.34
   C00104: €240.30
   C00105: €264.60
   C00106: €289.12
   C00107: €249.00
   C00108: €247.34

Exercise 6.2

1. 4591.44

2. 412.43

3. 4417.20

4. 858.92

5. 188.22

6. 579.54

Exercise 6.3

1. (a) 381.30
   (b) 66.55
   (c) 17.16
   (d) 297.59

2. (a) 400.00
   (b) 84.56
   (c) 8.60
   (d) 306.84

3. (a) 397.80
   (b) 83.48
   (c) 10.63
   (d) 303.49

4.

Employer's Name Mr Stephen Roche	PPS No. 3456.189A		Total Tax Credit €1110		Total Cut-off Point €14,800				
Month No.	Gross Pay	Cumulative Gross Pay	Cumulative Standard Rate Cut-off Point	Cumulative Tax Due at Standard Rate	Cumulative Tax Due at Higher Rate	Cumulative Gross Tax	Cumulative Tax Credit	Cumulative Tax	Tax Deducted This Period
1	€2400.00	€2400.00	€1644.45	€328.89	€317.33	€646.22	€123.34	€522.88	€522.88
2	€1600.00	€4000.00	€3288.89	€657.77	€298.66	€956.44	€246.68	€709.76	€186.88
3	€2000.00	€6000.00	€4933.33	€986.66	€448.00	€1434.66	€370.00	€1064.66	€354.90
4	€2500.00	€8500.00	€6577.78	€1315.55	€807.33	€2122.88	€493.33	€1629.55	€564.89
5	€3500.00	€12000.00	€8222.22	€1644.44	€1586.67	€3231.11	€616.67	€2614.44	€984.89
6	€2000.00	€14000.00	€9866.67	€1973.33	€1736.00	€3709.33	€740.00	€2969.33	€354.89
7	€2000.00	€16000.00	€11511.11	€2302.22	€1885.33	€4187.59	€863.33	€3324.22	€354.89
8	€2000.00	€18000.00	€13155.56	€2631.11	€2034.66	€4665.77	€986.67	€3679.10	€354.89
9	€2000.00	€20000.00	€14800.00	€2960.00	€2184.00	€5144.00	€1110.00	€4034.00	€354.89

CHAPTER 7

Exercise 7.1

1. (a) €35
   (b) €1 225
   (c) €2 600
   (d) €1 230.36
   (e) €78
   (f) €3120.16

Exercise 7.2

1. (a) €1 172.02
   (b) €56.20
   (c) €188.52
   (d) €193.60
   (e) €439.93
   (f) €58.00

2. €562.50

3. €18099.17

4. €467.25

Exercise 7.3

1. (a) €1.99
   (b) €3
   (c) €2.50
   (d) €69.99
   (e) €500
   (f) €149
   (g) €2.99
   (h) €4.50

2. (a) €3.00, €9.00
   (b) €6.00, €30.00
   (c) €1.95, €8.45
   (d) €14, €84
   (e) €70, €270
   (f) €2.25, €7.25
   (g) €90, €240

3. (a) €1450
   (b) €32.50
   (c) €550

4. (a) €15 000
   (b) €33 000
   (c) €26 000
   (d) €3 000

5. (a) €7 970
   (b) €16 240
   (c) €119 260
   (d) €91 072

Exercise 7.4

1. (a) €7.20
   (b) €16.65
   (c) €2.55
   (d) €27.00
   (e) €129.20

2. (a) €3.50
   (b) €1.47
   (c) €76.00

3. (a) €490
   (b) €780
   (c) €12 090
   (d) €8 400

4. €2210

5. (a) €450
   (b) €1152
   (c) €1584
   (d) €1014

Exercise 7.5

1. (a) €437.80
   (b) €1562.06
   (c) €328.00
   (d) €253.20
   (e) €362.50
   (f) €71.88

2. (a) €2.00
   (b) €49.40
   (c) €724.10
   (d) €8.93
   (e) €499.91
   (f) €544.43

Exercise 7.6

1. $1104.60

2. 595 834 Japanese Yen

3. 1251.93 SwF

4. 15 145.91 Est. KR.

5. 127.09 Can. $

6. €1791.76

7. €89.56

8. €5731.73

9. €4629.85

10. €6106.24

11. €5357.92

12. €5189.37

13. (a) €6411.76
    (b) €1125
    (c) €1508.20
    (d) €9950.25
    (e) 1804 600 Japanese yen

CHAPTER 8

Exercise 8.1

1. 28.98

2. 133.12

3. 55.62

4. 1066.13

5. 3058.44

6. 4918.95

7. 2105.63

8. 2130.56

9. 2119.15

10. 23 976.33

11. 2527.93

12. 386.40

Exercise 8.2

1. (a) 5050
   (b) 9521.25
   (c) 29230.76
   (d) 30190.88

Exercise 8.3

1. (a) 180
   (b) 900
   (c) 480
   (d) 453.25
   (e) 6472.48

2. (a) €2.45
   (b) €10
   (c) €2.50
   (d) €12

3. €827.50

4. €510

5. €89 285.71

6. (a) €350
   (b) €672
   (c) €960
   (d) €784

7. (a) €900
   (b) €160
   (c) €150

8. €926

9. (a) €370
   (b) €740
   (c) €485

10. €10 000

Exercise 8.4

1. (a) €6300
   (b) €750
   (c) €13 300
   (d) €114 000

2. (a) €3645
   (b) €72 392.13
   (c) €11 490.91
   (d) €2531.25

3. €12 266.50

4. Value   12 000
   – Scrap   2 000
   _____
                 10 000 ÷ 5
   _____

depreciation (dep) = 2000

	€
Motor van value	12 000
Year 1 dep	2 000
Value end of year 1	10 000
Year 2 dep	2 000
Value end of year 2	8 000
Year 3 dep	2 000
Value end of year 3	6 000

5.

	€
Machine value 1990	20 000
Year 1 dep	4 000
Value end of year 1	16 000
Year 2 dep	3 200
Value end of year 2	12 800
Year 3 dep	2 560
Value end of year 3	10 240
Year 4 dep	2 048
Value end of year 4	8 192

6.

	€
1994 motor van	20 000
Dep. 1st year	3 000
1994 value end of 1st year	17 000
Purchase of second van	15 000
1995 total value beginning 2nd year	32 000
Dep. year 2	4 800
1995 value end of 2nd year	27 200
1996 dep. 3rd year	4 080
1996 value end of 3rd year	23 120

Book value on 1 January 1997 was €23 120.

CHAPTER 9

Exercise 9.1

1. (a) 28 437
   (b) 10.12

2. 2 851.14

3. 3 933 750

4. $1\frac{5}{6}$

5. $1\frac{1}{4}$

6. (a) $\frac{11}{16}$
   (b) 157.89

7. $2\frac{10}{11}$

8. (a) 0.6
   (b) 0.33

9. (a) 63.21, 18.06
   (b) 8.60

10. (a) 2650.77
    (b) €30

Exercise 9.2

1. 1 420 710

2. 24 398.773

3. 385.25

4. €13 333.33

5. 799.90

6. 3 707.2

7. €180.50

8. 80%

9. €1 680

10. €31.25

Exercise 9.3

(a) 625 m²
(b) 140 m²
(c) 485 m²
(d) 10 kg
(e) €30

Exercise 9.4

(a) (i) €85
    (ii) €57

		€
(b) Income		255
	Expenditure	
	Fixed	
	Rent	55
	Insurance	8
	Irregular	
	Groceries	85
	ESB	10
	Bus fares	15
	Discretionary	
	Entertainment	25
	Savings	57
	Total expenditure	255

(c) €31.90

Exercise 9.5

(a) 47.4%
(b) 40%
(c) 36 students
(d) 28%

Exercise 9.6

(a) €180
(b) €115
(c) €21.96
(d) €31.05
(e) €126.99

Exercise 9.7

(a) 2.157 kg
(b) €7.65
(c) €10.71
(d) €12.85
(e) $13.44

Exercise 9.8

(a) 5 120
(b) 3 193.22